THE LION'S WHISKERS

Tales of High Africa

WITH ILLUSTRATIONS

BY

JAMES G. TEASON

LITTLE, BROWN AND COMPANY

THE LION'S WHISKERS

Tales of High Africa

by

Russell Davis

and Brent Ashabranner

BOSTON   TORONTO

Published simultaneously in Canada
by Little, Brown & Company (Canada) Limited

PRINTED IN THE UNITED STATES OF AMERICA

For Martha and Mary

Contents

Contents

Authors' Note

THIS is a book about the highlands of East Africa and about the people who live there. Most of all it is a book of the stories that the people of high Africa tell. We heard these stories from old village storytellers and from young school children, who had heard them from mothers and grandmothers. Sometimes we listened to the stories in smoky, dimly lighted native huts; sometimes they were told to us as we sat around a campfire in the high mountain country where nights are cold.

Of course our main job was not to collect stories. We were in Ethiopia to help the Ethiopian Ministry of Education prepare books for their schools. We did this for two years. Working with eager young Ethiopians, we helped to put out a series of primers, readers, arithmetic books, and other reading material for the schools of Ethiopia. In most cases these were the first such books that had ever been written for Ethiopian school children in their own language.

Gathering the materials for these books and testing what we prepared took us all over the country. It was in this way that we came to know the people and their stories. Many of the stories we had never heard before. Some we recognized as stories that had first been told hundreds of

years ago in Arabia or India. Somehow these stories had
found their way into the Ethiopian highlands, and the
Ethiopian people had made them their own.

We liked the people of high Africa and we liked their
stories. We think you will enjoy reading about the clever
Amharas, the dashing Galla horsemen, and the mystery of
the Falasha people. We are sure you will like the stories
of the turtle who talked too much, of the baboons who
tried to build a tower to God, of the man who lived three
hundred years on water alone. And these are only a few
of the funny and exciting stories of men and animals that
you will find in the pages ahead.

RUSSELL DAVIS
BRENT ASHABRANNER

THE LION'S WHISKERS

Tales of High Africa

ourselves and said, "We have heard that you have a great power over the wild hyena."

The old man pulled his white *shamma* closer about his shoulders. "It is true," he said, "but tonight the power burns low."

We took four copper Ethiopian coins and put them on a rock beside him. "Perhaps the power could be made to grow strong," we suggested.

The expression on the old wizard's face did not change, but he stood up. "It is possible," he said. "Come inside."

The room was small, but the feebly flickering kerosene lantern hanging from a eucalyptus pole across the ceiling only partially lighted it.

"Sit in the shadows," Mohammed Moshin said, "and do not speak." From a corner he took a pile of bloody sheep bones and sat down cross-legged in the middle of the dirt floor. We had expected him to chant or beat a drum or use other magic devices, but instead he began to talk just as if he were speaking to people outside. Now he was speaking Somali, but fortunately we understood enough of it to know pretty well what he was saying.

"Abdullah," he called, "are you out there? Maymoonah, I have a nice bone for you. Zachariah, are you hungry tonight?"

He called other names, and it was not more than a minute before we began to hear the soft padding of feet and low, deep-throated growls from the darkness outside. And then we saw them — more than a dozen huge, shaggy-coated hyenas moving restlessly back and forth in front of the *tukal* door. Occasionally, one would stop and peer inside and then suddenly jump back into the darkness in great fright.

"Maymoonah," the old man called, "I know you are there. Come in or I will give this bone to another."

This seemed to do the trick. One of the hyenas, a big buff-colored beast, halted in the doorway, and after hesitating for almost a minute, put her head into the hut. Mohammed held a meaty bone out to her and coaxed her softly. The hyena's eyes blazed toward the shadows where we sat, and she backed up a step. But then her hunger seemed to conquer her fear; she slunk into the room with the ugly, broken-back gait that all hyenas have and snatched the bone from the wizard's hand. Instantly she bolted through the door and out into the safety of the darkness. We could hear her crunching the bone in her powerful jaws, and the growls of the other hyenas grew louder.

Maymoonah's bravery seemed to give courage to the rest of the pack, however, for the giant called Abdullah came in at once when his name was shouted. After that they came in eagerly, and sometimes there were as many as three hyenas in the room at once. But always, as soon as they had their bone, they would scramble frantically through the door.

When the pile of sheep bones was finished, Mohammed called, "It is enough. Be gone." And instantly the sounds of growling and of restlessly padding feet were gone from the yard outside the little hut. The silence was complete.

It was then that the old wizard turned to us for the first time. "Tonight was not good," he said. "My friends were afraid because strangers were present. It is my custom to make them sit down and eat from my hand."

"We are amazed at what we have seen," we said. "Can you tell us how you do this thing?"

"I learned it from my father," Mohammed replied, "who learned it from his father before him."

"Is it magic?" we asked him.

"A kind of magic," the old man said.

"Can you do the same with any animal?"

"Of course."

"Even with a lion?" we asked.

"Yes," Mohammed said, "and even with a child, which is sometimes hardest of all."

"We do not understand," we told him.

The old wizard smiled. "Have you heard the story of the woman Bizunesh who could not win the love of her stepchild Segab?" he asked.

"No," we said, "but we would like very much to hear it."

And here is the story that Mohammed Moshin told us that night in the smoky, one-room *tukal* in the Ethiopian town of Harar:

THE LION'S WHISKERS

Bizunesh, a woman of the African highlands, married Gudina, a man of the lowlands. When Bizunesh went to the house of Gudina, she found that he had a son named Segab. Segab was a very sad boy because his mother had died of the fever.

Bizunesh loved Segab very much and tried to be a true mother. She mended all of Segab's robes. She patched Segab's shoes. She always asked him which food he liked best. And she always tried to save the choicest pieces of meat from the stew for Segab. But he did not thank her. He did not even speak to her.

Bizunesh and her new son, Segab, were often alone together in the house of Gudina. Gudina was a merchant and traveled with mule caravans to distant cities in the mountains and on the plains. When Bizunesh was alone with Segab, she would speak to him very kindly. "I have always wanted a small son. Now God has given me one. I love you very much." She often tried to kiss him.

Segab would run from her and shout in a cross voice, "I do not love you. You are not my real mother. My mother is dead. I do not love you. I hate you."

Bizunesh would try to cook the food that Segab loved best. But Segab would not eat the food. She mended his robes, and he would run through the thorn bushes and tear the clothes. He waded in the river and ruined his new shoes. Every time she tried to kiss Segab, he would run away from her. Often she cried alone in her room, and she longed for the day when her son would love her as she loved him.

One day Segab ran away from the house, and stayed in the forest until his father came and found him. When Segab came home, he would not let his stepmother kiss him. Bizunesh cried all that night.

In the morning, Bizunesh went to the cave of a very famous witch doctor. Bizunesh told the witch doctor about her new son who did not love her. She said, "You must make me a magic love powder. Then Segab will love me, as he loved his own mother."

The witch doctor said, "To make such a powder I must have the chin whiskers of an old and ferocious lion who walks in the black-rock desert beyond the river. Bring the whiskers to me."

"How can I do that?" Bizunesh asked. "The lion will kill me."

"I cannot answer that," said the witch doctor. "I know about love powders. But I know little about lions. You must find a way."

Now Bizunesh loved Segab very much. She decided that she would try to get the chin whiskers, danger or not.

Bizunesh crossed the river to the black-rock desert and

looked at the lion from afar. The lion was a fierce one. When he roared, Bizunesh was afraid, and she ran away home.

The next day Bizunesh came from her house carrying food. She placed the food on a rock a mile away from the lion and ran.

On the following day, Bizunesh brought food and left it only a half-mile from the lion. On the next day, Bizunesh left the food a quarter of a mile from the lion and watched him from a distance while he ate.

Finally, Bizunesh left the food only a hundred yards from the fierce lion. The lion saw her and growled in a friendly way. Bizunesh stayed while the lion ate the food. The next day she left the food fifty yards from the lion. Then, one day Bizunesh went right up to the lion and fed him. She watched the lion's great jaws fly open! Crash shut! She heard the sound of his teeth tearing through the meat. She was very much frightened. But she loved Segab very much. She shut her eyes and reached out and snatched the whiskers from the lion's chin. The lion hardly noticed the small pain of losing three of his chin whiskers. Bizunesh ran away to the magician's cave.

She was almost out of breath when she reached the cave. "I have the lion's whiskers," she cried. "Now make me the love powder, and Segab will surely love me."

"I will not make you any love powder," the witch doctor said. "You learned how to approach the lion — slowly. Do the same with Segab, and he will surely learn to love you."

When Mohammed had finished his story, we too were smiling. "Now we understand," we said. "Bizunesh learned that big things must be done a little bit at a time and that one must be patient for results."

"Yes," said Mohammed, "and that is the secret of my magic with the hyenas."

"You are a wise man, Mohammed," we said.

Again he pulled his *shamma* close about him, for the night was growing chill. "I am a very old man," he replied, "but I have gone to school for many years."

"School?" we repeated. We knew that even now there were few schools in the Somali country, and that when Mohammed Moshin was a young man there had been none.

"Not inside of a building," Mohammed explained, "but around many village fires where things are talked about and stories are told."

"We have heard many stories in Ethiopia," we said, "and have liked them."

"A good storyteller knows that you must like his stories," Mohammed said, "or you will not come again to listen. But he also knows that you must learn something from the stories or you will soon come to know that they are not worth listening to."

"Where do such stories as that of Bizunesh and Segab come from?" we asked.

The old man shrugged his shoulders. "Who knows?" he asked. "They have been told in my country for so long that no one knows who told them first."

Mohammed grew silent and we knew that he was tired. We said good night to him and left his *tukal*. As we walked to our Land Rover, our flashlight beam stabbed into the darkness. From many a bush it caught the bright yellow spots of large hyena eyes, silently watching.

We were in the high African country for over two years, and we lived and worked among many different tribes and heard many of their stories. We wrote these stories down, and they are the ones we will tell in this book. Such stories are called folk tales. You have perhaps heard the term "folk tale" and never really understood what it meant. Old Mohammed Moshin had never heard of the term, but he knew what a folk tale was—a story that has been told in some country so long that no one knows who told it first; a story that you like to listen to and that makes you just a little wiser than you were before you heard it.

Every country, including our own, has its folk tales. In America we have dressed them up and put them into books and cartoons and motion pictures, but at one time the tales of Davy Crockett and Johnny Appleseed and Pecos Bill were told around the campfires, just as the tales of high Africa are today.

TWO

The Habasha and the King of Kings

Nοτ long ago, the country that is perched on top of the East African highlands was called Abyssinia. Now it is called Ethiopia. The name *Abyssinia* came from *Habasha,* the name of the people who had a great kingdom in the northern part of the country over fifteen hundred years ago. The new name Ethiopia came from a word meaning "people with burnt faces." It is the modern word for the country, and the people in it are Ethiopians. Many different people make up Ethiopia. There are Amharas, Gallas, Tigriñas, Somalis, Danakils, Guragies and many other tribes. Over fifty different languages are spoken in Ethiopia.

Sometimes the people of Ethiopia are divided into three great families, according to their languages: the Semitic people; the Hamitic or Cushitic; the Nilotic. Each of these big families has smaller families or tribes. The

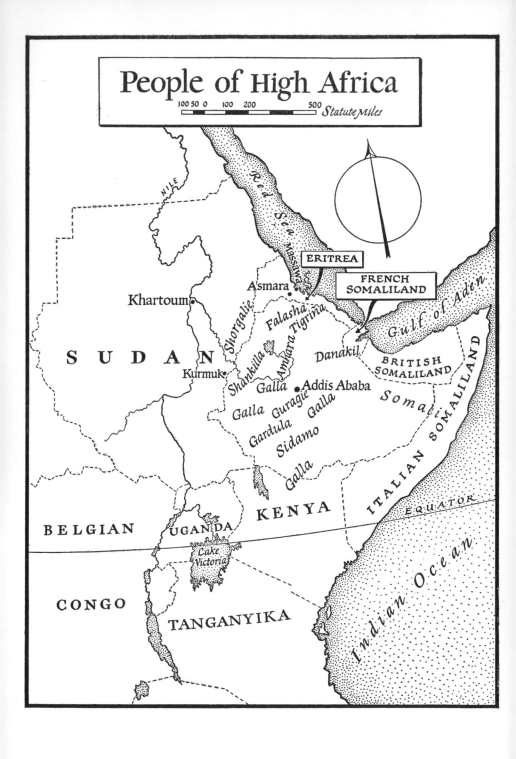

languages of these tribes are usually so different that the people of neighboring tribes cannot speak to each other.

Each tribe and language family has its special stories. Since the official language of the country — the national language by law — is Amharic, the language of the Amharas, it is fitting to begin this book with the folk stories of the Amharas. The Amharas are the mountain men of the central and western parts of the country. More than any other people, the Amharas rule Ethiopia. The Amharic language is used in the schools and in government business. The Amharas fill government jobs in all parts of the country.

If the Amharas govern Ethiopia, then the man who governs the Amharas, and all other Ethiopians, is His Imperial Majesty, Emperor Haile Selassie, King of Kings, the Conquering Lion of the tribe of Judah — and other titles too numerous to list here. Haile Selassie claims descent from the Queen of Sheba, the beautiful Ethiopian queen who traveled with her rich caravan all the way to ancient Israel to win the heart of King Solomon, richest and greatest of ancient kings.

When we think of queens and emperors, we usually think of people like Sheba and Solomon, who live only in history books, storybooks, or legends. We think of men and women who lived long ago and far away. It is hard to know whether or not to believe in kings at all. Sometimes they seem like fairies or giants or ancient gods, something invented to make stories more interesting. There are stories of King Midas and King Arthur and King Richard the Lion-Hearted, but these stories go so far back in time that we wonder if these kings really ever lived at all. Most Americans in their lifetime never see a king and never expect to see one — except, perhaps, on television!

Yet a great king and emperor does live today. He lives as surely as King Richard and Charlemagne and Alexander the Great once lived. This king, Haile Selassie, rules Ethiopians with a wisdom and greatness that the kings of the past might envy. Haile Selassie, King of Kings, Lion of Judah, and the rest of the titles, may be the last of the great kings. Before telling any more of our stories of high Africa, we will tell a true story, the story of Haile Selassie. Let us see how the Emperor passes his days, where and how he lives, and how he does his job as Emperor.

AT HOME WITH THE KING OF KINGS

THE house — that is, the *palace* — of Haile Selassie in Addis Ababa is nothing special. There are great houses in England and the United States that are as rich and fine as the Emperor's palace. But the palace is a fine house, all the same. It is on a straight broad avenue that runs past the palace and on up to Entoto Mountain. The street is broader and straighter than streets in Boston, but not any broader and straighter than streets in Salt Lake City. And the palace? There is a high wall and an iron-grilled gate with the imperial coat of arms on it. Soldiers with bayoneted rifles stand at the gate. Beyond the gate is a drive that winds between bright gardens, and there is a fountain and a pool. The palace is made of stucco and cement. It has even begun to crack at the corners. Inside are twenty-five rooms, some of them larger by far than a schoolroom. There are red carpets and drapes and paintings of kings and soldiers. After all, it is a palace and an emperor lives there.

But it is not his palace that marks Haile Selassie as something rare and special, nor is it his appearance. He is not a huge man. Once in the history of Ethiopia there was a giant Moslem king named Ahmed Gran, who invaded the country. Ahmed swung his huge sword and African heads rolled. And Ahmed wore a big red cape that is now in an Ethiopian museum. If Haile Selassie were to put on the cape of Ahmed Gran, the little Emperor would disappear from sight. Haile Selassie would not have reached up

to the belt buckle of Ahmed Gran, the Moslem giant.
But Haile Selassie is a far greater man, and history will
show that. History marks a man, not only for being a
great destroyer like Ahmed Gran and Genghis Khan, but
also for being a great builder.

Haile Selassie sometimes dresses in elaborate uniforms
with medals and epaulets and decorations; sometimes in
an explorer's sun helmet and a cape; and often in a plain
dark suit, like a businessman. But house, clothes, and size
do not make this man. It is what he does every day that
makes him a great man. What does the Emperor, the
King of Kings, look like in action?

The Emperor's day begins early. By the time the sun
comes up, he has already been at his desk for well over an
hour. We can skip over the early part of the Emperor's
day. Probably he does as we do. He wakes and says his
prayers; he washes and dresses and greets his family.
Sometimes early in the morning he reads and signs official
papers. He writes orders for the government and plans
talks with officials who direct the army or the treasury or
the diplomatic corps. As his day goes on, he becomes
busier and busier.

In the middle of the morning a large — but not very
new — limousine arrives at the door of the palace. Emperor Haile Selassie is now setting off on his public day
as Emperor. As he goes down the drive and through the
main gateway, soldiers snap to attention and salute. A car
full of soldiers — members of the Imperial Body Guard
— follows the Emperor's car.

As the limousine swings onto the main street, an old

man from the country, dressed in a long white robe called a *shamma,* runs screaming toward the Emperor's car. The old man beats on the top of his head, waves his arms, and screams. He runs right in front of the Emperor's car and it stops. The car full of soldiers stops. The old man whoops and throws something at the open car window. A bomb? No. The Emperor knows his people. The Emperor does not even duck when the wild old man throws something at him. He knows that the old man is throwing no bomb. He is throwing a piece of paper called a petition. He isn't trying to kill his Emperor. He just wants to get his attention. Perhaps the old man wants a government job for himself or his son. Perhaps he served in the army and wants land, or he may be complaining about his taxes. As Emperor of fifteen million Ethiopians, Haile Selassie cannot see every one of them. But he does see many of them. And those that he cannot see often run at his car and attempt to throw papers in to him. If he sees the old man's petition and if the petition is just, the old man may get what he asks for.

But the old man bothers the soldiers of the Body Guard more than he bothers the Emperor. The soldiers are charged with protecting the Emperor's life. The Emperor may not fear for his life, but the soldiers fear for him. The soldiers jump out of their station wagon and run toward the old man, who is hanging onto the fender of the car. One burly sergeant seizes the old man, spins him around, and runs him off to the side of the road. On the sidewalk the soldiers shake their fingers or their fists at the old man. The life of the Emperor is a serious trust.

The car is again ready to start. But the driver is afraid

to start. An old woman has flung herself under the front
wheels. She is dragged away by the soldiers and by police,
and the Emperor's caravan at last begins to move.

All along the sidewalk, Ethiopians bow low to the Emperor. Foreigners stop their car, jump out, and bow to His
Imperial Majesty. Even Americans, not very much used to
bowing, bow to Haile Selassie. Some Ethiopians throw
themselves face down on the sidewalk, and strike their
foreheads on the pavement. A line of Galla horsemen pile
off their ponies and whoop like Indians. The Emperor answers the bows by leaning forward in his seat. He dips his
head in a slight nod. He smiles to some. A little American
girl dips in a curtsy to the car, and the Emperor bows to
her.

First stop for the Imperial cars is a hospital. There are
more than five hospitals in Addis Ababa, the Emperor's
capital city, and most of the hospitals are named after the
Emperor or his family. Why does the Emperor get so
many hospitals named for him or his family? It is because
he supports the hospitals with money or gifts. The Emperor is visiting a new wing of the hospital. An American
doctor explains how the wards will be arranged. The op-
erating room will be over there. The Emperor notes each
detail. He gives a suggestion to one of his aides.

And then the Emperor gets quickly into his car. Outside the hospital gate more crowds have gathered, and the
limousine can scarcely get through. There are more people waving papers. All Ethiopians seem to have petitions.
All wish to put them before the Emperor. Away from the
hospital and to a government office. The Emperor shakes

hands quickly with the officials. He asks questions. They give answers. Away from that office goes the limousine.

There is a new school to visit. The Emperor is the father of Ethiopian schools. Before Haile Selassie there were no government schools. Now there are hundreds, and the Emperor has visited a good many of them. He goes through the grounds. He asks the British architect questions. Aides are pointing to their watches. Already the Imperial party is late for the next visit.

A stop at one more office, and then back to the palace offices. But not to rest. Outside the offices there is a long line of government officials. Each of them has pressing business. The Minister of the Pen has a list of new appointments for approval. The Minister of the Treasury has facts and figures. The Minister of Commerce has business of the Airlines. There is a conference with the Defense Ministers about the army. Telephone calls come in from governors and officials in the provinces.

There are dispatches from foreign diplomats. There is even the foreign news, which a modern ruler must read every day. There are appointments to be made, jobs to be filled. An army unit is on special parade, and a quick trip must be made to review the troops. The line outside the offices never goes down. People wave papers inside the palace and out. Sons of important people and Ethiopian students returning from foreign schools must be interviewed. These newly educated Ethiopians will be the future leaders of the country and the Emperor speaks to all of them. He must judge all of them. He must give each of them a talk that will make them want to work for their country as he does. There is the funeral of an important official to attend. The Bishop of the Ethiopian church must see the Emperor. There are medals to be awarded.

There is another trip in the limousine, again to a school. Every child in the school is lined up on a field. The Emperor speaks briefly to the students and then personally hands out gift sweaters to them. Row on row of children wait to come forward for their gifts. Ethiopians love and expect gifts and their Emperor is supposed to be the biggest giver.

Back in the palace there are more reports and still a line of waiting people. Taxes were not good in Illubabor. An American has advice on foreign affairs. A Britisher comes to talk about the police. Judges come with difficult cases. A Frenchman discusses Ethiopia's one railroad. An important British army officer who fought with the Emperor against the Italians is passing through Addis Ababa. The Emperor must see him. The Emperor must also talk with an Italian embassy official.

At night there is an important dinner. Speeches must be read and listened to. Reports wait to be read. People will be back in the morning, waiting in the corridors. We would expect that by the end of the day Haile Selassie's head must swim with waving papers. Before his eyes he must see endless lines of waiting officials. Whatever the Emperor dreams, if he dreams, it must be a busy dream. Like his day it must be filled with thousands of papers. The Emperor is trying to build his country. He tries to do in fifteen years what other countries have taken hundreds of years to do.

The thing that makes the Emperor different from ordinary men is that the Emperor must know a little bit of what every man in the Empire knows. The Emperor must do a little bit of what every man does. Above all, the Emperor must share every man's troubles and worries. The Emperor must work harder and longer than any man — and he must work without hope of reward and promotion. There is no place for him to advance to. He is at the top. He can only go down, never up.

Kings and emperors have their problems. If you have no treasure, you have no worry about guarding it. Here is an old Ethiopian story that illustrates the problems of kings.

THE SNAKE IN THE BOTTLE

A KING out of the west traveled north and south and east and fought great battles and took much treasure. Since the king was always away at war, he built a great treasure room and hired a man to guard it.

Now the guard of the treasure room was very careful to keep others from stealing the riches of the king. But the guard himself began to steal the king's treasure. For many years the guard took the treasure, little by little, to a storehouse of his own. The guard emptied the chests of gold and silver and jewels and filled them with stones and pebbles.

When the king was old and crippled from his wounds, he returned to his palace to enjoy his treasure. The guard came before the king and said, "Now Your Majesty has

returned. There is a lion in the house once more and so
no need for an old guard such as I. Who can guard the
treasure better than you, my King?"

"You have spoken the truth," the king said. "And you
have served me well for many years. Take this great chest
of gold and go on your way. Live your remaining days in
peace and plenty."

After the guard had gone, the king discovered that his
chests were filled with stones and pebbles. The king sent
horsemen out to bring back the dishonest guard. The
guard tried to escape into another country. But the king's
territories had grown very large, and the guard's many
mules were heavily laden with gold and treasure. The
horsemen found the guard still within the kingdom and
spoke to him: "His Majesty bids you return to his palace.
He wishes to speak to you."

"Why does he wish to speak to me?" the guard asked. "I have done nothing."

"He has not given us any reason," the soldiers said. "But you must return."

When the guard returned to the palace, the king told him to sit down in the throne room. "I would like to tell you a very short story," he said. "Once a snake crawled into a farmhouse and found an open jug of milk. The snake crawled in through the narrow neck of the jug and began to drink all of the milk. The snake drank and drank until he was too fat to crawl back through the neck of the jug."

The king stopped speaking and smiled.

"Is that the end of the story?" the guard asked. "I have a long journey and I would like to be off."

"That is not quite the end," the king said. "What must that snake do to get back out of the jug?"

"The snake must spit out the milk," the guard answered.

"True," the king said. "Should he spit out all of it?"

"I think he will have to spit out all of it to get out," the guard said.

"You are very right," the king said. "All of it."

The guard looked up and saw soldiers with spears moving slowly toward him from every door of the throne room.

We can imagine that the guard gave back all of the treasure, just as the king suggested in his little story about the snake trapped in the bottle. It is easy to see why the king did not just order the guard to give back the treasure. Instead the king told a story of a thieving snake. The king wanted to teach the guard a lesson with the story of the snake.

There is no telling whether the guard ever escaped from the throne room, even if he promised to give back the treasure. Like many good stories, "The Snake and the Bottle" leaves the reader with something to think about.

Another folk story of the Amhara people shows that a good king must be a fair and wise one.

THE KING'S BLACK CURTAIN

M ANY years ago Ethiopian kings were considered to be almost gods. For this reason it was thought to be improper for anyone, even a nobleman, to see a king eat. In the king's banquet hall there was a long table for the noblemen and a smaller table for the king. Whenever the king sat down to eat, a black curtain was always put up in front of his table so that none of the noblemen could watch him eat. The king could talk to his guests and they could talk to him, but he could not be seen until after the meal was over.

On one particular feast day the nobles of the court were gathered at the palace arguing about who would be seated nearest the king's table at the dinner that night. It was considered a great honor to be seated near the king, for then it was possible to talk to him throughout the meal, even when the curtain was drawn across his table. This arguing among the noblemen went on every time there

was to be a feast. It was pointless arguing, however, because the king always made up his own mind who would
be seated nearest to him.

On this particular day a very well-known teacher came
to the king's court. This teacher was famous throughout
the land for his wisdom and for the truth of his teach-
ings. Nevertheless, he was a humble man who had never
before even been to the king's city.

The noblemen were surprised to see a mere teacher at
the court, and one of them said to him laughingly, "Have
you come to join the feast?"

The other nobles laughed at the idea of a teacher, however wise, attending the king's dinner.

The teacher himself smiled at the question. "No," he
said, "I have only come to pay my respects to the king and
to bow before him, for I believe that he is a great and
good king."

Some of the noblemen thought that the king would not
even take time to see the teacher; but when the king
heard that the wise old man was at his palace, he sent for
him at once. The noblemen then went back to their arguing and forgot about the teacher.

When they gathered for the feast that night, the nobles
were greatly surprised to see that the king had asked the
teacher to attend the dinner. But when the nobles sat down
at their long table their surprise turned to shock and anger, for the teacher did not sit down with them. Instead
the king took the old teacher by the arm and led him behind the black curtain to eat at the king's own private
table!

One of the bolder noblemen rose and called out in a complaining voice, "Oh, King, never have you given such honor to even the greatest of your nobles. Why do you give this honor to a poor teacher?"

The king came from behind the curtain and all of the nobles rose from their chairs. "Who made you a *ras?*" the king asked the man who had complained.

"You did, Sire," the man replied. "You gave me that title."

The king pointed to another nobleman. "Who made you a *dejazmach?*" he asked.

"You did, Sire," the man answered.

The king pointed to still another. "Who made you a *kenyazmach?*" he asked.

"You did, Sire," the man said.

The king looked at every nobleman in turn and asked, "Who made the teacher behind that curtain the wise man that he is?"

The noblemen looked at each other and none could answer this question.

The king then said to them, "I can create noblemen. I can take any poor man from the street and give him a title and make him rich and powerful. But only God can create such a wise man as the teacher who eats with me tonight. For this reason is his honor greater than yours."

The king went back behind his black curtain where the teacher awaited him. The nobles sat down again and fell silently to eating, ashamed of the jealousy that had angered them.

THREE

The Amharas:
Rulers of High Africa

WE have visited the king of all Ethiopians. Let us visit the Amhara people on the high plateaus and mountains, and listen to the stories of mountain people.

The Amharas are not the largest group of people in Ethiopia. There are far more Gallas than Amharas. But the Amharas are the Ethiopians that most visitors to the country remember. Sometimes the memory is pleasant, sometimes unpleasant. The Amharas are the officials of Ethiopia, the governors, the mayors, the soldiers, the clerks and the policemen. Originally the Amharas lived in the provinces of Gojjam and Begemdir, the provinces that lie beyond the mighty gorge of the Blue Nile River. Then they pushed south into Shoa, the central province of Ethiopia, where Addis Ababa is. Now the Amharas live in the towns and villages in all parts of the Ethiopian highlands. In some cases the Amharas have even moved down the hillsides and live in the lowlands among the Somali and Galla tribes.

To be honest, the Amhara is not loved by other tribesmen of high Africa. The Amharas take the better jobs in the Ethiopian government. They can be good friends but they are dangerous enemies. The Amhara is proud, quick-tempered, and changeable.

The food of the Amharas is *wot,* a spicy stew made of chicken, lamb, or goat. With the *wot,* they eat *injera,* a round, flat cake made of a grain called *tef* (millet). *Injera* is more than a food. It also serves as a spoon, fork and table napkin. The Amhara uses the *injera* to scoop up the *wot* or to get a grip on the meat. He does not eat with his fingers; he eats with his *injera* in his fingers. After the meal he mops up the sauce in the dish with *injera.* Then he wipes his mouth and hands on the left-over pieces of *injera.* Not that Ethiopians are careless about washing their hands before and after meals. They always do so.

Once an American who was a guest at an Ethiopian banquet took the fold of *injera* that was beside his plate and spread it on his lap like a napkin. The Ethiopians were very much amused. They would have been more amused if the American had tucked it under his chin. The American was not far wrong, though. *Injera* looks like a big brown napkin and serves as a napkin.

In addition to milk and water, the Amharas drink *tej* and *talla. Tej* is a yellowish liquid that is made from fermented honey. It can be a very strong drink. *Talla* is a beer made of grain, and it is not half so powerful a drink as *tej*. Hundreds of years ago, the ancestors of the British made a drink from fermented honey — like *tej* — and they called it mead. Mead was the drink of the knights of King Arthur's Round Table.

Most Ethiopians of other tribes would call the Amharas "tricky." The Amhara calls himself "clever." The Amharas are the city slickers of Ethiopia. Their stories are filled with what they like to call "cleverness," and what other people call "dishonesty." But no such word ever applies to every member of a large group of people. Some Amharas are as honest and dependable as any people in the world.

The language of Ethiopia, by order of the government, is Amharic, the language of the Amharas. Other tribal languages, or at least writing in other languages, is discouraged by the Ethiopian government. To attend school, an Ethiopian child of any tribe must learn Amharic. Amharic, like the languages of Tigre, Tigriña, Guragie and Adari, came from an ancient Ethiopian language called G'eez. G'eez came from the same language family as Hebrew or Arabic. Today G'eez is only used as the language of the Ethiopian church. The official foreign language of Ethiopia is English, which almost all educated Ethiopians speak.

The stories of the Amhara tell mostly of trickery — cleverness! The next story will illustrate this. One of the Ethiopian's favorite characters is a "clever" monkey. What is meant by "tricky" depends on whether your sympathy is with the trickster or the tricked. Of three thousand

Ethiopian stories which we collected, the greatest part of
them had tricks in them. Here is a classic Ethiopian
story type — clever monkey.

THE BOB-TAILED MONKEY AND
THE KING'S HONEY

A KING of Shoa brought a beautiful lady of Gojjam Province to be his wife, but the new queen was not happy in
her home in Shoa. She complained of the lamb, the goat,
and the chicken that she bought in Shoa to make the
king's *wot*. The queen also complained because the honey
of Shoa was not as pure as the honey of Gojjam, and for
this reason she could not make good *tej*. Day after day
the queen nagged and scolded the king: "In Shoa the
chickens are crossed with vultures, the lamb and goats
look like hyenas, the honey is dark and dirty. I must return to my Gojjam where everything is clear and pure."

To keep his queen happy, the king promised that he
would have sheep and goats and chickens brought from
Gojjam. When the queen still was unhappy, the king arranged, at great cost, to have honey carried from Gojjam
to Shoa. The promise of honey made the queen as happy
as any Gojjam woman ever could be if she had to live in
Shoa.

A merchant of Fiche was hired to bring the honey from
Gojjam to the queen's kitchen in Shoa. It was not easy to
bring the honey down from Gojjam, for the way led
through the deep gorge of the Blue Nile River. When it
rained in the east the road was hard to travel, and mud

came up to the withers of a mule. One dark night as the merchant and his servant drove their mules through the mud, the bowl of the sky turned upside down and rain poured down on all the earth.

The merchant and his servant wandered off the road and were lost. They could find no house to shelter them, and they drove the mules into a great forest. Deep in the forest the rain still dripped down on them through the trees. The merchant and his servant huddled down in their blankets and cursed the rain.

A monkey came along the forest path and saw the merchant and his mules. The monkey sniffed at the packs on the mules, and he knew that the merchant was bringing Gojjam honey into Shoa. The monkey greeted the merchant, "Ay, Merchant, have you no head? Here you sit, wet and sad, in this terrible forest. And I have a home that is snug and warm. For a moment I could not tell you from your mules. Oh, that is your servant there. I thought he too was a mule. Come to my house and be warm by my fire."

"Thank you," the merchant said. "But what of the mules and our precious honey?"

"I will tie them outside my house," the monkey said. "It is too wet for robbers to be outside tonight. Do not worry."

"Be careful where you tie them," the merchant warned him. "I carry this honey for the queen's kitchen in Shoa."

"Do not fear," the monkey said. "I will tie them well."

The merchant and his servant followed the monkey to

his house. The monkey tied the mules to a tree outside
the house. Then the monkey put a sharp stick in the middle of the path. "Usually I would not tie mules," he said.
"But the night is so wet that all the world belongs to the
crocodiles. They will come out of the river and swim
across the land. The stick is for them."

The merchant found the monkey's house snug and
warm. The monkey hopped about the house, pouring
cups of *tej* for the merchant and his servant. "This is a
very good *tej*," the merchant said.

"I use only the finest Gojjam honey in my *tej*," the monkey said. "My wife will not make *tej* with any other
honey." The monkey poured out cup after cup of *tej*, but
he brought no food to the merchant. "We will eat when
my wife returns," the monkey said.

The night passed, and the merchant had drunk a great
deal of *tej*. He had not eaten any food, for the monkey's
wife never came. The servant lay down by the fire, and
soon he was snoring. The monkey said to the merchant,
"I see you are yawning and blinking your eyes. Is there
something strange about the way I look?"

"I have drunk too many cups of *tej*," the merchant said.
"I looked at you now and my eyes played tricks on me. It
seemed to me that you had no tail."

Now it was true that this monkey had no tail. But the
bold monkey said to the merchant, "Your eyes tricked
you. I have a tail. All monkeys have tails. But there is a
reason why the *tej* makes you think that I have no tail.
Would you like me to tell you why you think that I have
no tail?"

"Yes, tell me why," the merchant said sleepily. "I would like to hear the reason."

"Well, this is the reason," the monkey said. But before the monkey could say another word the merchant was snoring on the floor. The monkey watched the sleeping merchant for a moment, and then he went out of the house to where the mules were tied. The monkey opened the packs and tried the honey with his finger. It was pure Gojjam honey. The monkey emptied the honey jars into his own jars, and filled the merchant's jars with mud from the river. The monkey then went back into the house and fell asleep.

In the morning the merchant woke. He did not speak to either the monkey or to the servant. The merchant and the servant drove the mules back onto the road and on toward Shoa. As he watched him go, the monkey said, "What a rude man. He never even thanked me for my fine *tej*."

When the merchant arrived at the king's palace there was great joy. The queen smiled for the first time, and the king was happy. The jars were unloaded from the mules and carried into the queen's kitchen. The queen lined up all her servants and spoke to them: "The honey of Gojjam is the best in the world. The honey of Shoa is like mud. I wish all of you to taste the difference, so that you may know what good honey is."

The queen made all of the servants dip their fingers in the pots and taste the honey of Gojjam. (Each servant, then, tasted the mud that the monkey had put there.)

"Is it not the best honey?" the queen asked each servant in turn.

Each servant put his hand over his mouth after tasting the mud, but each of them said to the queen: "Oh, it is fine, Your Majesty. It is not at all like the mud of Shoa."

The queen smiled happily and at last dipped her finger into the pots and tasted what was in them. "Poison!" the queen screamed. "It is poison. You fools, why did you not tell me?"

The king shouted. The guards roared and clashed their swords and shields. The poor merchant was seized as he went out through the gate of the palace.

"This is a terrible thing," the king bellowed at the merchant. "You have tried to trick your king. And you have tried to poison your queen. And you have stolen royal honey. Death for you, Merchant!"

The merchant screamed and begged and swore by Saint This and Saint That. "I am innocent. The monkey tricked me. It was the monkey. He stole the queen's honey. The bob-tailed monkey should die."

"Aya, good," the king exclaimed. "You are a rogue. I have heard fine lies before. But you are the first to blame your crime on a monkey. And on a monkey with a short tail. What of this bob-tailed monkey, Merchant?"

The merchant told his story. He beat on the ground with his forehead, and he swore by Saint Tekle-Haimanot and Christos that he spoke only the truth.

"It will be easy to get to the truth," the king said. "If the bob-tailed monkey is found, I will free you at once. Such a story is worth a few days more life to you. You will go into the forest with the soldiers and search for the bob-tailed thief. Now, Merchant — one more question. Did this bob-tailed monkey know that the honey was for the queen?"

"Yes, I told him so. I told him to be careful of the mules because they carried honey for the queen. But he gave me much *tej,* and no food. I was tired from the road and I slept. While I slept, he stole the honey and replaced it with mud."

"That is very bad," the king said. "That makes it an insult against the royal family." To the soldiers, the king said, "If you find a bob-tailed monkey, this merchant will be free. When you find the monkey, kill him. If you find no bob-tailed monkey, kill the merchant. Go!"

The merchant and the king's soldiers traveled into the forest. When they entered the forest, they scared all animals before them with the sound of drums and swords. The monkeys and all the other animals fled before the sound of the army. The monkeys ran to the deepest part of the forest. "Why are they hunting us?" the monkeys wondered. "We are of no use to man. We have nothing he wants. Our fur is poor and our meat is thin."

"They hunt us for our tails," the tricky monkey told the others. "All the ladies of the palace carry monkey tails now. For this reason they will kill us and cut off our tails."

"What can we do?" the monkeys wailed. "They will kill us and cut off our tails."

"You do not have to die," the tricky monkey said. "Notice that I have no tail. Because I have no tail, they will not kill me to get my tail. Therefore, you must cut off your tails. Then you will not have to worry."

"But we need our tails," the monkeys protested. "We use them when we are sitting in trees and eating with our hands."

"You can learn to do well without your tails," the tricky monkey told them. "I've learned to get along without my tail. Which of you eats better than I? I can climb and sit as well as any of you. But why should I argue with you. I have no tail. I'm safe."

The other monkeys believed the tricky monkey, and they all cut off their tails. Several days later when the soldiers found the monkeys, none of them had any tails. All the monkeys were bob-tailed, and tricky monkey looked just like the rest.

"What did I tell the king," the merchant cried. "This more than proves my story. Not just one monkey is bob-tailed, all monkeys here have cut their tails. So we have found, not just one, but a hundred bob-tailed monkeys. And I will go free."

The soldiers did not know what to do. It was true that the king said the merchant was to go free if they found a bob-tailed monkey. The soldiers released the merchant. He began to run, and late that evening he had arrived in Debra Markos.

The soldiers could not kill all of the monkeys. Therefore they marched back to Shoa to get orders from the king. "Did you find the bob-tailed monkey?" the king asked.

"We found hundreds of bob-tailed monkeys," the captain of the soldiers said. "The merchant spoke the truth many times over. All the monkeys in the forest were bob-tailed. We released the merchant as you told us. But we could not kill so many monkeys."

"It is a trick," the king shouted. "But who has played the trick? Is it the merchant or the monkey?" The king consulted his wisest advisor, the man who advised him on wars, love, and tricks.

"The monkey played the trick," the wise man said. "There is a clever one among them, and he stole the honey. This one saw the soldiers and the merchant seeking him. He got the other monkeys to cut off their tails so that he could not be chosen from the others. That is the one we seek — the monkey who lost his tail long ago."

The soldiers, the wise man, and the king traveled into the great forest. Again the monkeys ran from the army and hid in the deepest part of the forest. For days the soldiers wandered through the forest, seeking the monkeys. At last the monkeys could run no farther, and the soldiers caught them. The soldiers caught several monkeys and brought them to the king. "We are defeated," the king said. "Now we cannot tell which was the monkey who lost his tail long ago. This monkey is too clever for us."

"No monkey is too clever for me," the wise man said. "I have a test. It will tell us which is the guilty monkey. The soldiers must force all of the monkeys to sit on the branches of the trees that surround this clearing. Give the monkeys no food for three days."

For three days the monkeys sat on the branches. The monkeys shivered, cried and moaned, but they were given no food. On the third day, the king cried out, "Now your king will give you a grand feast. I wanted you to be hungry enough to enjoy it."

The soldiers carried many plates of food into the clearing. At a signal from the king, the soldiers began to throw the food toward the monkeys. All of the monkeys but one tried to catch the food with both hands and hold on with their tails, as they had always done. Since their tails were gone, of course they all fell from the tree branches to the ground. Only the clever monkey did not fall off. He clung to the branch of the tree with one hand and caught the food with his other hand.

"There is the guilty one," the wise man said. "He is the monkey who lost his tail long ago. He has learned to hold to the branch with one hand. Seize him!"

"I am innocent," the monkey cried. "How do you know that I lost my tail long ago? Perhaps I lost it only recently but learned faster than the others because I am more clever."

"That proves it anyway," the wise man said. "Only you would be clever enough to trick the merchant. We were seeking a clever monkey with a bob-tail. You are the one."

The soldiers tied the monkey's hands and feet and staked him down to the bank of the river. "The crocodiles will come," the king said. "You will steal no more royal honey."

The soldiers hung a sign on the monkey: *Do Not Touch, by Order of the King.* Then the soldiers, the wise man, and the king marched back to Shoa. This time they sang a victory song.

In the evening a hyena came to the river to drink. He saw the monkey and the sign, and he was puzzled. "What does it all mean?" the hyena asked the monkey.

"Isn't it clear to you?" the monkey asked. "The sign means that I am under the protection of the king. This is a test of my courage. If I stay here all night, the king will give me a whole cow."

"A whole cow?" the hyena asked.

"A whole cow," the monkey said.

"How could a little monkey like you eat a whole cow?" the hyena asked.

"That is the sad thing," the monkey said. "This good luck should never have come to me. I can't eat a whole cow. I don't need a whole cow. But good fortune always comes to those who need it least."

"If I took your place could I get the reward the king promised you?" the hyena asked.

"I'm sure of it," the monkey said.

The hyena untied the monkey and the monkey tied the hyena to the stake. The monkey swung up into the branches of the trees above the river bank. "You will not need the sign," the monkey said to the hyena.

"Why will I not need the sign?"

"Crocodiles can't read," the monkey said. Then he added loudly, "Eat well."

"Thank you," the hyena said. "I will."

"I wasn't talking to you," the monkey said. "I was talking to the crocodiles."

The clever monkey story is a great favorite of the Amharas. They use it to show that a clever person can never be defeated. He always has one last trick up his sleeve. In this version of the story, one thing is missing — the monkey's tail.

The story doesn't explain how the clever monkey lost his tail in the first place. In Ethiopia there are stories with a hundred different endings, but the bob-tailed monkey is a story with a hundred different beginnings. In each different version, the monkey loses his tail in a different way.

In one story the monkey and a leopard own a water hole together. They charge other animals to drink at the water hole. The leopard takes a holiday away from the business, and the monkey tries to cheat the leopard out of his share of the money collected. The leopard chases the monkey to the high branches of the tree. As the monkey escapes, the leopard's sharp claws take off the monkey's tail. The monkey shouts back, "You've got the harmless end of me, Mr. Leopard. I injured you with my head and not my tail. Keep my tail; it will serve you well as a head."

In another version the monkey is in partnership with a lion. When the lion goes away, the monkey cannot make the big animals pay for using the water hole. The lion thinks the monkey has cheated him, and rips off his tail.

The monkey then says, "When I had my tail I was honest and yet I suffered. Now I will be honest no longer. I will be like a man."

In one story the monkey is born without a tail. The monkey's mother is horrified when she sees that her baby has no tail like other monkeys. "He is a human monster," the mother cries. "This is not my baby. It looks more like a human." The other monkeys drive the freak monkey out into the world of humans. Living with humans, the poor, tail-less monkey has to learn many dishonest tricks to live. Finally the monkey returns from the land of humans to the land of monkeys. The monkey has now learned many more tricks than his monkey brothers. So the tail-less monkey becomes king of all the other monkeys, and they work for him.

Sometimes this story is just turned around. A human is forced to live among the beasts of the forest. He learns the ways of the beasts so well that he returns to rule as king of men.

So much for clever monkey, favorite of the Amharas. Like many folk stories clever monkey has some truth to it. The monkeys of Africa — perhaps because of the trick of the bob-tailed monkey — do not use their tails as much as monkeys that live in other parts of the world. Many African monkeys have rather short tails. But this tale is long enough, as it is.

Let's tell one about a gold-lined donkey.

THE GOLD-LINED DONKEY

SOUTH of Irgalem, Sidamo country is very fertile. The earth is dark; the fields and trees are always green. Once a man of Sidamo carried a sack of grain from the market to his home. There was a hole in the sack, and as the man walked, the grain spilled bit by bit to the ground. When the Sidamo man arrived home, he walked behind his house and left the half-empty sack of grain in the storage bin. In the morning a great field of grain had grown up from the grain that had spilled from the sack the night before. The grain grew so high that the Sidamo man could not find his way back to the market. He could not find his way to the water well. The man died, wandering around in the field of grain, trying to find someone to make him a loaf of bread. Yes, the Sidamo country is rich, and the Sidamo men are lazy. A merchant of Debra Sina heard all this and came to the country to set up his shop.

This merchant of Debra Sina grew very rich in the Sidamo country. For although the land is rich, the men do not work their fields. They would rather buy grain than grow it.

Even though he made much money, the merchant of Debra Sina was not happy. He grew sad watching so many lazy men to whom God had given good land, bright sunshine, and much rain. He found that he could sell anything to these men. He could sell good grain and bad grain, fine cloth and coarse cloth. Whatever the merchant put in his stall for the Saturday market, he sold to the foolish people.

The merchant often tried to talk to the Sidamo people: "God sends rain and sun to your fields. Work your land. Do not sit about the market square like fools. Men should work their fields. If not, they are the same as animals."

But the Sidamos only laughed at the merchant and lined up in front of the stall to be cheated.

The merchant grew sadder every day. There was no joy to his business. To be always among fools made him dull and spoiled his life. While he was still young, the merchant went back to the north to bargain with his own people. He enjoyed this. He was often cheated by the people of Shoa, and this made the merchant happy. He would return to Sidamo and be happy for a while, thinking of the joy of bargaining back in his own village. But as he grew older the merchant could not make the long, hard journey north. He was forced to stay always among the foolish villagers. Will nothing ever teach these foolish people a lesson? he wondered.

One day the merchant had a fine idea. He took one of his oldest and most broken-down donkeys from the field. He placed three gold coins in the donkey's mouth. Then the merchant brought the donkey into the middle of the Tuesday market. The merchant cried out in a loud voice, "Gather round me, men of Sidamo, and you will see a marvel. I am old, and I am rich, as you know. Soon I will die. I can take no gold under my wings. Hear me then. Why am I wealthy? See my hands. Have they ever held a hoe or spade? Never. I am rich because I have this wonderful gold-lined donkey."

At the merchant's cries, all of the shiftless villagers gathered around. "Watch closely, my friends," the merchant said. "If I need gold, I have only to pump this donkey."

As the people watched, the servant of the merchant pumped the donkey's tail up and down. The merchant held his hand under the donkey's mouth. Out came a gold piece.

"Would any of you good people like to try it?" the merchant asked.

Several of the stupidest fellows rushed to the tail end of the donkey to pump, but one rich landowner came to the head of the donkey to gather the money. The villagers pumped the tail, and out dropped another gold piece. The landowner held up the coin for all to see. "It is a wonder," the landowner said. "I will buy this marvelous beast."

"Not so fast," the merchant said. "I will sell it to the man who pays me the most for it. That is business."

All of the Sidamos gathered around and began to shout for the gold-lined donkey. The bidding for the donkey grew higher and higher. Finally the merchant sold the donkey at a great price to the landowner and his rich brother.

The merchant collected his money and went back to his stall to watch. "First let us get our money back," the rich landowner said. His brother pumped the donkey's tail, and the third and last gold piece fell out into the landowner's

hands. "Take it," he said to a poor old woman who stood
in the crowd.

"Now, brother," the landowner said. "I will hold this
empty sack at this end. You pump at the other."

The landowner spread open the sack, and his brother
began to pump. But no gold came. The landowner raced
to the rear of the donkey and began to pump, and even to
twist the donkey's tail. But no gold came. The villagers
pumped and beat on the donkey but no gold came. The
merchant, who had watched them, and who knew that
all three coins were gone, began to laugh at them from
his stall.

The landowner shouted and wailed and screamed at the
merchant. A great crowd gathered in front of the stall.

"You have cheated us," the brothers cried. "We do not mind small cheating. It is too hard to read weights and make change. But this is very big cheating."

"I have not cheated you," the merchant said. "Like everything there is a secret to the gold-lined donkey. You must know the secret. Once you know the secret, the donkey will produce gold again."

"Tell us the secret," the landowner begged. "We bought the donkey."

"You bought the donkey. You did not buy the secret. You will have to pay another hundred pieces of gold to get the secret."

"We have no more gold," the landowner wailed. "You have all our gold. Tell us the secret, and we will pump your hundred pieces of gold out of the donkey."

"That is impossible," the merchant said. "You must get me the gold first."

Two other rich men agreed to pay the hundred pieces of gold. The four Sidamo men agreed to share the gold from the donkey. They brought the money to the merchant.

"Now," said the merchant, "the secret is simply this. To get gold from the donkey, you must put gold into the donkey. Watch me closely."

The merchant put two gold coins into the donkey's mouth. The servant pumped the donkey's tail, and the donkey produced one coin after the other. The merchant took his two coins and walked back to his stall. He was feeling very gay. He called to the Sidamo men: "Now you try it. Remember the secret. If you put gold in, you take gold out. And there is no cheating. You always get exactly as many coins out as you put in."

The Sidamo men did as the merchant said. The landowner put in two gold coins, belonging to a friend, and then pumped them out again. "It is true," the landowner cried. "If you put gold in, you take gold out."

"Have I lied to you?" the merchant asked.

"No. You have told us the truth. It is as you say."

"Have I cheated you?" the merchant asked.

"No. You get exactly what you put in. No more, no less."

The merchant closed his stall and went away to his house. In the morning he almost ran to the market. These slow fools will have learned the trick by now, the merchant thought. They will realize that I have tricked them again. They will be very angry. And now I can teach them a lesson. Now these foolish Sidamos will learn that you do not get gold for nothing. Now they will learn that they must put into their land what they expect to take out. Oh, how angry they will be. The merchant hurried on into the market.

But the merchant found no angry crowd in front of his stall. Instead, all of the villagers were gathered around the marvelous donkey. People from other villages had heard of the donkey and had come to see it. News of the wonderful donkey had spread to all of the markets in the district. The merchant saw in the crowd the landowners who had bought the donkey. The landowners were not angry. They were laughing and shouting and jumping with happiness. People struggled to get close enough to see the wonderful donkey perform.

One landowner yelled at the merchant over the head of the crowd, "My friend, it is all true. It is as you said. This animal is a wonderful thing. You have made my brother and me the happiest men in the district."

Every day on his way from the stand to his house, the merchant passed the crowd around the gold-lined donkey. Always people laughed and cheered and were happy there. The merchant tried to sneak by the crowd without looking at it. But always he turned to look. He would shake his head and walk on.

One day the merchant did not wish to come to his stall. He stayed in his home. He blocked the doors and windows and would not come out. His servants tried to get him to come out to eat, but the merchant would not. A day came when the merchant could not come out. He was too sick to come out and too sick to cry out. He died in his dark house.

When word of the merchant's death reached the village, the people came to his house. They pointed to it and said to the people from other villages, "That is where our good merchant lived. He is the man who brought the gold-lined donkey to this village. It is a pity that he is dead now. God always takes the good to His heart."

Some of the people of the village wished to have the donkey march in the funeral procession of the merchant. But the priest of the village was against this. "I am not sure that this would be a fitting thing," the priest said.

Two old and kindly priest teachers told us the story of the gold-lined donkey. Each man told us a part of it.

They disagreed with each other on the story's meaning.

One of the teacher-priests said, "The meaning is clear. No man can be all bad. But some men are all foolish. Notice that the cheating merchant tried to teach the people a lesson with the donkey. But the people were too stupid to learn it. The story is a strange one in many ways. Why do we have one of our churches among such people? It said there was a priest there."

The other priest said, "I think the end of the story was this: Take a fool's money and he laughs; take a fool's foolishness and he dies. I agree that it is a strange story. Why was that merchant sad? Was he not rich? And the part about the donkey and the procession. A man may have his horse there. Why not his donkey?"

"It was no longer *his* donkey," the first priest said.

"Ah, that is true. Perhaps that was the reason."

A third man was listening to the story in the schoolhouse. "I think neither of you understood the story right. The merchant died because he realized that he could have made much more money by keeping the donkey. He could have shown the donkey to the foolish country people. They would have paid much to see it. But he had sold him."

"Not true," the teachers argued. "That merchant died because his heart was broken. He wished to teach a lesson, and the foolish people would not learn it. As schoolteachers we can understand why he died. We often feel like dying for the same reason. Nobody ever learns."

"I have a question," another man said. "Who was the

real fool in this story? Was it the happy people or the unhappy merchant?"

If someone answered this last question we did not hear it.

Amhara children and grown-ups enjoy the adventures of a clever midget called Sinzero. The name Sinzero comes from the Amharic word *sinzer,* the measure of the distance from the tip of the thumb to the tip of the longest finger. We have translated the name Sinzero to Digit in our story, although the actual translation of the word would be span. The span is still used as a measure of length in Ethiopia, and it was once used in England and America.

Actually, there are two midgets in Ethiopian storyland. The other one's name is Aure Tat, from the word for thumb. One of the most famous midgets in America was Tom Thumb, who traveled with the circus. Both of the Ethiopian midgets, Tom Thumb and Digit, appear in hundreds of stories. We've chosen only one of the stories for this book.

DIGIT THE MIDGET

A WOMAN of Munz had seven large, strong, stupid sons. These sons went about the house breaking chairs with their weight, emptying the *injera* basket and the *wot* pot with their great appetites, and filling the house with the terrifying rumble of their snoring. Although they were

very strong they never worked when they could avoid it.
They ate, slept, snored, and got in the way of their poor,
hard-working mother.

One day the poor woman of Munz could stand her
house and family no longer. She ran away toward the
Monastery of Saint Stephen on an island in Lake Haik.
The woman was not allowed to go out to the island and
the monastery. No woman had been allowed there since
the monastery had been built hundreds of years ago. The
woman from Munz knelt down on the lake shore, cast her
eyes toward the holy monastery on the island, and cried
in a loud voice, "Oh, God and all Your Angels and Saints,
hear my prayer. I have been sent seven of the biggest,
clumsiest, hungriest, and laziest sons in Ethiopia. Soon I
am to have another child. I would like a daughter. But
if You do not wish to send me the daughter, send me a
small son."

Now God, Who hears all prayers but only answers some,
did not send a daughter, but He did send a very small son.
When Digit was born he was only half the length of a
man's thumb. The woman of Munz was delighted with
her little child. It was the first baby she had ever been
able to carry in her arms. For all the other babies, the
mother had had to hire a mule to bring them home.

When the days passed and Digit did not grow larger, the
mother was even more pleased. And it was clear to her that
Digit was a very clever baby and, later, a clever little boy.
Digit had to be clever to dodge the feet of his huge, clumsy
brothers. Often Digit's mother barely saved him from
being crushed by one of his brother's elbows. Another time,

when the door was left open, Digit was blown out into the yard by the breeze of his brothers' snoring. Digit's mother always kept him close to her, safe from mice and chickens.

As the years passed, the seven huge brothers came to hate Digit. Even when they had been babies and sick, their mother had never taken them on her lap. Their mother had never kissed them on the top of their heads. She had never even seen the tops of their heads. She had never hugged them because her arms would not fit around them. And once when the oldest brother hugged his mother he broke three of her ribs. It was clear that Digit was her favorite. She took the choicest meat from the *wot* for Digit, and the brothers had to crack the bones and pick out the marrow for him.

The brothers plotted and schemed to get rid of Digit. Once they persuaded him to steal the prize bull of their most terrible neighbor. The brothers thought that the terrible neighbor, who was a *cherak,* or man-eating monster, would catch and eat Digit. But Digit climbed into the bull's ear. When Digit wished the bull to turn right, Digit buzzed like a horse fly in the bull's left ear. The bull then turned right to escape the fly. To make a left turn, Digit walked all the way across the bull's neck and buzzed in the right ear. Digit took the bull right out from under the cherak's nose and guided it to the forest where the brothers waited.

The brothers were sorry that Digit escaped, but they were happy to get the bull. They made a big fire and killed and dressed the bull. The brothers then took all the choice meat for themselves and left Digit almost none.

Digit said, "Brothers, you are big men and you need the food. All I wish for is the bladder."

The brothers threw the bladder to Digit. Digit then puffed air into the bladder and made a drum. He began to beat on the drum with a stick and shout, "We stole your prize bull, Cherak. Come and get us if you dare. My big brothers aren't afraid of your evil spells."

The brothers were so frightened that they threw the meat on the ground and ran away into the forest. Digit went back to the cherak's house, stole a mule, and loaded the meat onto it. Digit brought the mule and the meat home and gave them to his mother. The mother made a stew of the hoofs and tail for the brothers.

Things grew worse between Digit and his brothers. The brothers complained, "Mama never hugs and kisses us. Does she ever call us little stalks of sugar? Never. With the little fiend gone, Mama would love us again."

Finally things became so bad that Digit had to move out of the house to his own little house. The mother was so angry that she made the brothers leave their home and get married.

One night the brothers came and burned Digit's house. But Digit was not killed. He slipped through a hole in the floor into the tunnel of a rabbit. Digit walked through the tunnel to safety.

The next morning Digit loaded the ashes of his house into sacks and had the sacks loaded onto mules. Digit decided to leave Munz to escape his brothers. On the road the first night Digit stopped at the house of a rich man. In the morning when Digit looked into his sacks, he began to scream, "Robbery! Thief! Some thief took my flour and filled the sacks with ashes."

Digit screamed and screamed, and the rich man felt very sorry for the poor little boy. The rich man did not want his neighbors to think that he would steal flour from a midget. So he gave Digit seven sacks of new flour. Digit decided to return home to give the flour to his mother.

When Digit returned home with the flour he told his brothers how he had tricked the rich man. "A very clever trick," all the brothers agreed. They went back to their own houses, burned them down and loaded the ashes onto the mules.

The first brother went to the home of the rich man and spent the night. The next morning he opened his sacks of ashes and began to scream that he had been robbed — just as Digit had done. But the rich man ordered him out of the house. When the second brother came along the next day and tried the same trick, the rich man had his servants throw him into the road. When the third brother came, the rich man ordered his servant to beat him with sticks.

When the fourth brother came to the house, the rich man asked, "What do you have in those sacks?"

"Flour," the stupid brother said.

"That is good. We are short of flour. We'll make your bread tonight from that flour."

That night the brother had to eat ashes bread, and the next day he was driven from the house. The rich man played the same trick on the fifth and sixth brother. But when the seventh brother came by, the rich man was tired of his joke. He turned the dogs loose on the seventh brother.

The brothers gathered around the bed of the seventh brother. "Digit must die," they decided.

One night while their mother and their wives slept, the brothers took Digit, pushed him into an *injera* basket and carried him to the river. The brothers tied down the lid of the basket and threw it into the river. They were certain that they would never see Digit the Midget again.

But the current of the river carried the basket along and washed it up on the shore. In the morning an Arab merchant named Yusef found the basket and opened it. Out hopped Digit. He began to dance and sing, "Oh, you are lucky. You are Allah's favored son."

"Why am I lucky?" the Arab asked. "I have only found a wet little boy on a river bank. What is lucky about that?"

Digit said, "Do I look unusual or strange?"

"You are unusually small," Yusef said.

"Yes. I am very small. For this reason I am the messenger of Allah. But for my small size I could not have fitted into this magic basket. And what a magic basket this is! Each day at noon it fills with gold."

Yusef was interested in a basket that filled with gold, but he was also greedy and worried. He said, "If I took that basket back to the town, the governor would take it from me."

"That is true," Digit agreed. "That is why Allah sent it to this wilderness."

"I have an idea," Yusef said. "I will stay here until the basket fills with gold many times. Then I will load the gold on mules. First I will hide the basket up in those rocks. I can give the governor some of my gold and come back for more whenever I need it."

"You are wise," Digit agreed. "It is a pleasure to find a man who is not so overcome with greed that he stops thinking. That plan sounds good. Where are your mules?"

The merchant struck himself on the forehead and began to pull at his beard. "What do I say! Fool, fool that I am. I sold my mules back at the last village and bought this fine horse to sell to the Sheik Mustafa."

"Very well," Digit said. "I will stay with the basket and the gold. You ride your fine horse to the village and bring back mules."

"Oh, no," said the greedy Yusef. "I will stay with the basket. You take this money and my horse and go for the mules. But you must tell no one about the magic basket."

"I will tell no one," Digit promised. "But do not worry. Only a very stupid man would believe such a story from a little boy."

Yusef laughed. "That is true," he agreed. "No one would believe such a story. Go, and be quick about it."

Digit took the money from the merchant, and climbed hand-over-hand up the horse's tail and onto the saddle. "I must tell you one other thing," Digit said. "You are new to the basket. If it does not bring gold on the noon of the first day, do not worry. You must be patient. The gold is worth waiting for."

"I will be patient," Yusef promised. "There will be thousands of noons to come. The first one does not matter."

Digit left Yusef sitting in front of the basket, and watching for the sun to reach the middle of the heavens. The horse was swift and strong, and Digit was at his home that night. Before giving the horse to his mother, Digit let all of his brothers see the horse and ride on it. But Digit would not tell them where he got the horse. He showed them the merchant's money and said that he had had many horses and sold them to get the money. Digit also gave the money to his mother.

"Why do you giant fools never bring me money or horses?" the mother screamed at her sons. "You bring me nothing but trouble. If it were not for the little one, we would all starve." The mother's words did not please her sons.

That night while the brothers filled the house with the rumble and thunder of their snoring, Digit crawled to the bed of his oldest brother. To his brother Digit whispered, "I found the horses in the river where you threw me. There are many more there. Tomorrow while the others still sleep we will go there. When I whistle it will be the signal to rise and go to the river."

Digit then crept to the bed of his next oldest brother. "I found the horses in the forest. I tell only you of this. Tomorrow we will go there. I will whistle. Rise and follow me to the forest."

Digit told the next brother that the horses were on the mountain. To the next brother, Digit said that he had found the horses in the lake. He told the next brother that he found the horses on the desert, and the last brother was told to go to the meadow.

While the brothers were sleeping, and dreaming of horses, Digit tied all of their legs together.

In the morning Digit gave a shrill whistle through a hollow tube. The brothers rose and began to run in seven different directions. Enraged, because they were tied together, they began to strike out and kick at one another. Finally they beat each other senseless.

Digit said to his mother, "I go after more horses."

"And where will you find them?" she asked.

"Wherever fools ride them," he told her.

There is no end to the Digit story. And no end to the stories about Digit. We found over a hundred different stories of Digit the Midget. In one series of stories, Digit became a house burglar. He entered the house by riding underneath a cat.

Unhappily, we found no story in which Digit reformed and became an honest midget. Digit went on looking for fools who could be tricked out of their horses. You could say one thing for Digit. He was always good to his poor old mother.

TO OUTLEAP A RABBIT

A HYENA and a jackal lived and worked together. They lived in peace under one roof, worked together in one field, and shared their food. The hyena had an old bull that was used for heavy work. The jackal had a young cow that furnished milk for their table.

One day a rabbit, who came from the north, stopped at the house and asked to speak to the jackal. "I bring you sad news," the rabbit told the jackal. "Your mother, who lives in my forest, is very sick. Since I traveled far to the south, she asked me to tell you of her sickness. You must go to her at once if you wish to see her alive."

"I would do that gladly," the jackal said. "But it is such a bad time. My cow will soon bring forth a calf. I do not wish to leave her now."

"What kind of a son are you?" the hyena said. "Go to your mother when she calls you. I will take care of your cow and calf."

The jackal set off for the north to visit his mother. The rabbit went on to the south where he was to enter a jumping contest against a cheetah.

The new calf was born, and it was a beautiful animal, but the cow died. At first the little calf was sick, and the hyena had to nurse it day and night. The hyena came to love the calf a great deal. How soft are its eyes, and how smooth is its skin, the hyena thought. I have all the care of this little one. It is as my own child.

One day the jackal returned from the north. "I am so sad," the jackal said. "My mother died."

"I have no news to cheer you here," the hyena said. "Both your cow and your calf died from the fever."

The jackal began to weep. "All is lost to me. Both the new and the old are gone."

"All is not lost," said the hyena. "Perhaps God wished to console us with a miracle. The day after your cow and calf died, my old bull brought forth a pretty, new calf. Be not sad. When my calf grows up, I will share the milk."

As the days passed, the jackal grew suspicious of the hyena. The new calf never went near the old bull, who was supposed to be the mother. The new calf often cried in the night, like a child with no mother.

"My cow was the mother of that calf," the jackal said to himself. "The hyena tries to trick me."

The hyena noticed that the jackal was growing suspicious. One day he will try to claim my calf, the hyena thought. He only waits until the calf becomes a cow and gives milk. The hyena decided to sell the calf and keep the money, although it broke his heart to part with the beautiful animal.

When the hyena said that he was going to sell the calf, the jackal said nothing. But the jackal followed the hyena and the calf to the market place. When the hyena brought the calf to the cattle ground, the jackal began to shout, "This hyena is a great thief. He has stolen my calf, and now he tries to sell it." All of the animals gathered round. It was a Wednesday market, and only the small animals were there. The small animals gathered in a circle around the hyena and the jackal and the calf.

"Tell your stories," the animals shouted.

"It is my calf," the jackal said. "A rabbit brought news that my mother was sick in the north. At that time I knew that my cow was going to bring forth a calf, and I did not wish to leave. But this greedy hyena said that he would take care of my calf. When I returned, the hyena said that both my cow and my calf had died of the fever. The hyena said that his bull brought forth this calf."

Some of the smaller animals began to giggle. But the hyena showed his great teeth to the small animals, and they were quiet. "This jackal breathes lies into the air," the hyena said. "His calf died as I told him it did. And perhaps God wished to reward us for his loss. My bull brought forth this calf, and it is a true miracle."

The little animals laughed, but the hyena walked close to them and rumbled, "Do you not believe in God and His miracles? What kind of animals are you?"

"We believe, we believe," the little animals cried.

"Your sin is double," the jackal told the hyena. "First you steal. Then you lie and swear that it is the work of God. You are a wicked animal, and God will punish you. My cow was to bring forth a calf. The rabbit will tell you that."

"Who has seen such a rabbit?" the hyena asked the other animals. The hyena curled his lip and showed his teeth to the monkey, the mole, and the dik-dik, tiniest of all gazelles. "Did you see such a rabbit?" the hyena asked them.

"We saw nothing. We have only the jackal's word for the rabbit."

"Where is your rabbit?" the hyena asked. "We see no rabbit here."

"He has gone to the south to jump against the cheetah," the jackal said. "He was a brown rabbit with white marks."

The hyena laughed and the other animals joined him. "All rabbits look like that."

"And he was a great jumper in the north," the jackal said.

"All rabbits are great jumpers," the hyena said. "What animal can outleap a rabbit and out-lie a jackal?"

Now the small animals were very much frightened by the hyena, but still they were afraid to decide the case. Judge Elephant was not there, and nothing could be judged in that village without the elephant.

"We must wait for Judge Elephant or the rabbit to come," the jackal said. "We must respect the law. Besides, he will trample you all if you decide without him."

"That is true," the animals said. "We must respect the law. We will wait two days. In this village we love the law. But if the rabbit does not come in two days, the hyena takes the calf. And he may sell it if he wishes."

"I will buy it," the monkey offered.

Two days passed. A dove flew to the south to see if either Judge Elephant or the rabbit was coming. But neither was coming. The animals gathered in the market place to make the award to the hyena. The monkey rose first and made a long speech.

"We must all love the law," the monkey said after his long speech. "Justice must be done to this hyena, and I will give three jars of honey and twenty measures of grain for this poor, sick, worthless calf."

The animals began to cry that the award should be made. The hyena showed his yellow teeth and growled. The jackal wept. But before the hyena could take the calf, the rabbit jumped into the middle of the market square.

"This calf belongs to the jackal," the rabbit said. "He has spoken the truth."

The hyena ran over to the rabbit. "You have taken a long time to come before us. You are not dependable. Who should believe you?"

"I would have been here sooner," the rabbit said. "But the earth opened up so wide, even I could not jump across it. I had to walk around the crack in the earth."

"Silly story," the hyena snarled. "In what country does the earth open up so wide that a rabbit cannot jump across?"

"In what country does a bull bring forth a calf?" the rabbit asked.

The animals began to laugh, and they awarded the calf to the jackal.

The jackal was so happy that he ordered a great feast to celebrate. He even invited the greedy hyena. During the meal, the rabbit saw the hyena looking at him across the table. I must eat my food quickly and be on my way north, the rabbit thought. This hyena will surely kill me for appearing against him. The rabbit ate his food as quickly as he could, but as the rabbit left the village, he heard the hyena running after him.

"Now I have you," the hyena called. "You should know better, Rabbit. Never get in an eating contest with a hyena. I can eat faster than any animal."

The rabbit ran for the river, but the hyena was gaining on him. The rabbit ran to the widest part of the river and jumped across. The hyena tried to jump across and fell into the water.

"Never get in a jumping contest with a rabbit," the rabbit called.

Just then a huge crocodile rose from the river bed and seized the floundering hyena. "And never get in a swimming contest with a crocodile," the crocodile said.

So much for trying to outleap a rabbit. We have a saying in English that sums up the story of the rabbit and the hyena: "Never try to beat a man at his own game."

THE SMILING INNKEEPER

To an inn near Filowha (Hot Springs) there came a rich farmer from the country to take the mineral baths and cure his sickness. The innkeeper of Filowha was a man who never worried about his own health. He made his living sympathizing with other people about their sickness. When the farmer came to the inn, the innkeeper put him in a miserable room that had no windows. The country man did not complain about the bad room. He was tired from traveling, and he slept at once.

In the middle of the night he awoke. His room was completely dark. "I am blind!" the country man cried. "I am blind, blind, blind!"

The innkeeper tiptoed through the darkness to the room of the rich farmer. "Stop crying out," the innkeeper said. "You will wake everyone in this house."

"But I am blind," the farmer screamed. "What can I do now? I have much land. How can I see that my servants work my fields? I have many cattle. My servants will steal them from me. What can I do?"

"Is it true that you cannot see me standing here?" the innkeeper asked.

"It is true," the farmer said. "My sickness has made me blind. I was afraid of this."

"I think I can make you see me," the innkeeper said.

"If you can do that," the man said, "I will give you everything."

"I am a merciful man," the innkeeper answered. "I will do it for two fat cows."

"I promise you ten," the farmer said. "Make me see. Bring me your special waters."

"You don't need waters to make you see," the innkeeper said. "You need light."

He ordered a light to be brought from the kitchen, and the farmer saw the innkeeper very clearly. The innkeeper was smiling.

The innkeeper could afford to smile after earning ten cows that easily. Even in Africa people worry about their health, and there is always a dishonest person ready to make them pay for their worry. People who worry about their health when they are not sick are called hypochondriacs. They have them in Africa as well as America. When we were in Africa our medicine chest was always empty. The servants would take all the pills they found, whether they could read the labels on the box or not.

Perhaps the story of the smiling innkeeper isn't so funny to some people. Some of us do not like jokes about blindness. But the African can joke about almost anything, no matter how serious.

Most of our Amhara stories have been about tricksters. Here is a story that is different. "Lion Bones" has passed back and forth among all the tribes. Somewhere in some African or Arab or Indian village some clever storyteller first thought of "Lion Bones." Whoever that storyteller was, we would like to say, "Thanks for a good story."

LION BONES AND
THE GARDULA MAGICIANS

An Amhara farmer went to the southwest in Gamu-Gofa to look for good land. Near Gardula the land was fertile, but nobody planted crops there. The Gardula tribesmen were more interested in magic than in farming. The people thought that anyone could be a good farmer but that only very wise and skilled men could be good magicians.

The Amhara farmer listened to many wonderful stories of magic and magicians. But always he said, "The greatest magic is God's magic. He turned the forest and plain into a garden for our father Adam. Why do you not practice this magic? Then I would marvel. Then I would admire you."

One day the farmer was walking through a forest, and he met three of the greatest magicians of Gardula. The great magicians said that the farmer could walk along behind them if he was quiet and did not try to talk. The farmer agreed to be silent. The Gardula magicians told many wonderful stories. Each tried to tell a more wonderful story than the others. As they walked through the forest, they came upon the bones of a lion. The bones had been picked clean by the vultures, the hyenas, the ants and the sun.

The first magician said, "Watch closely now, Farmer.

I can put these lion bones together just as they once were." The magician bent down and put the bones together and formed the perfect skeleton of a lion.

"That was easy," the second magician said. "I can put flesh on these bones and make a real-looking lion." The second magician did this.

"Wonderful," the farmer said. "But a lion is not a lion without his fierce spirit and his roar."

"I can fix that," the third magician said. "I will breathe a lion's spirit into this lifeless body. I will make the lion roar."

"And I will climb a tree," the farmer said.

The farmer climbed a tree, and the third magician breathed spirit into the lion.

The lion stood up, blinked, shook himself, roared — and ate the three magicians.

From the tree the farmer watched and said, "Truly, the magicians of Gardula are very clever."

FOUR

The Only People

DANAKIL! This word has struck fear into the hearts of people over most of Ethiopia. The Danakil are nomads who wander over the hot desert wastes of northeastern Ethiopia, and they have had the reputation of being the most savagely ferocious tribe in the whole of high Africa. All of the peoples whose lands border the desert — the Tigrians, the Gallas, the Somalis, the Adiras — have known the terror of a Danakil raid at night. They used to raid sometimes for cattle, camels, and children; sometimes for revenge; sometimes for the sheer love of fighting. They are still a fiercely proud people and look with scorn on all other tribes. In Dankali, the language they speak, their name for themselves is *Afar,* which means the Only People.

The Danakil are slender and small-boned, but the men have a look of wiry toughness. Most Danakil men wear long, wide-bladed knives which curve at the end and

taper to a wicked point. They carry their knives in leather
sheaths, which are often colorfully decorated with dyes
and bright metal. Some Danakil men also have rifles;
usually the rifles are older than the men who own them,
but they are always kept in perfect working order. Dana-

kil men never waste precious bullets hunting animals.
The guns are kept only for fighting.

The Danakil people lead an extremely simple life.
They grow no crops, even along the life-giving Awash
River that cuts through their desert land. They lead their
goats and sheep from place to place seeking grass and
water, and they carry their tiny houses with them on their
camels. These houses are made of two or more straw
mats stretched over slender wooden hoops. When a house
is set up, it looks very much like half of a rubber ball
sitting on the ground; the house is very easy to take apart
so that it can be lashed on the camel along with the
family's few belongings — blankets, milk and water con-
tainers, a little clothing, perhaps.

The Danakil people live almost entirely on milk; they
are equally fond of goat milk and camel milk. They
seldom eat vegetables or bread, and they eat meat only
when one of their animals dies or is too feeble to travel
with the herd. They can drink more than a gallon of
milk at a time, and they never get tired of it. They keep
their milk in skin bags and in baskets of tightly woven
grass.

No one works very hard in a Danakil village, and men
don't work at all. Once a day the women milk the
animals and once a day they go to the river or oasis well
for water. The children watch the goats and camels to
see that they do not stray too far away while they are
grazing, but the youngsters still have plenty of time to
play. The men do little more than sit in the shade of
their grass huts and talk to each other. Some people think

this is why the Danakils once raided by night — they had nothing to do all day but sit around thinking up mischief.

Although the Ethiopian police force is stronger and better organized today than it has ever been, the Danakil warriors still go on occasional raids against neighboring tribes. The brave fighters among the Danakils once received all of the honor and glory and were given heroes' burials if they happened to be killed in battle. In the old days a Danakil was not considered a man until he had killed at least one person of another tribe. Even today many Danakils wear a secret mark that means they have killed one man or more.

But even among these remote and fierce people there are signs of change. A Norwegian friend of ours, after four hard years, has finally got a school going in the oasis town of Asiata — the first school ever to be built in the Danakil country. When we visited the school, there were three classrooms of children, and our friend said that they were all bright students. It is only a small start toward education, but every year more and more Danakil families are driving their cattle to the Asiata oasis so that their children can stay for a few months and learn to read and write the magic marks on paper.

You would expect Danakil stories to deal with fighting and the importance of being strong or of knowing your strength. That is just what they are about. In our first story the old lion is, of course, the Danakil, and the hyenas are all of the other tribes. The point of the story is a very common Danakil belief — to the strong goes everything. It is the kind of story you might hear any night around the campfires of the "Only People."

THE LION'S SHARE

In the Batie foothills where they slope down to the flat Danakil plain, there lived an old hyena and his nine sons. Although the old one was in good health, he preferred to stay in their cave day and night — to guard it, so he said — and send his sons out to hunt for food. Still, he took his duties as a father seriously, for he talked to his sons constantly about what a brave hunter and strong-hearted fighter he was. He made it clear that he expected his sons to follow in his footsteps.

One evening the nine sons went out together on their daily search for food. They had not gone far through the underbrush when they were unexpectedly joined by a great tawny-maned lion who lived in the neighborhood. The hyenas were about to slink away by themselves when the lion stopped them.

"Just a minute, friends," he said. "Why don't we hunt together tonight? I've been searching for two hours and haven't found a thing. With your sense of smell and my strength we might get something good; then we'll split it."

The hyenas would have been much happier by themselves; but since no one wanted to tell the lion this, they all went with him. Luck was with them, for almost immediately the hyenas' sharp noses led them to a tree where a hunter had tied a bag of freshly killed guinea hens, expecting to return for them later. He had not tied them quite high enough, however, for by stretching to his full height the big lion was able to pull the bag down.

They tore it open eagerly and pulled out the guinea hens. There were exactly ten of them. "You see how wise it was for us to hunt together," the lion said. "Now we shall share the food."

He selected the nine fattest birds for himself. The one undersized guinea that was left he tossed to the hyenas. The hyenas all howled in protest, and the lion frowned slightly at the noise.

"What's the matter?" he asked, looking at each hyena in turn. "Didn't I divide them right?"

The hyenas were afraid to answer him, so after a moment the lion picked up his nine fat birds and walked off toward his den. The unhappy hyenas, knowing that their father would scold them if they did not return soon with food, picked up their thin little guinea and returned to their cave.

When the father saw the miserable night's haul, he made an angry speech about lazy, inconsiderate sons that lasted almost half an hour. "And do you really expect me to make a meal out of this mouthful of feathers?" he asked scornfully.

"Father," said one of the sons, "we had a very fine dinner for you, but the lion's share was bigger than we thought it would be." The son then went on to tell how they had hunted with the lion and how he had divided the guineas.

The old hyena was beside himself with rage, even before his son had finished. He called them cowards, weaklings, ingrates, and several other names. Then he turned his angry words against the lion and worked himself into such a frenzy that his sons were afraid he would fall into a fit.

At last his anger was so great that he quite forgot himself. Picking up the guinea he started out of the cave and said to his sons, "Follow me. I'll go to that lion and exchange this sparrow for our fair share of the birds. I'll see that justice is done. Be glad your father is brave enough to face him."

They reached the lion's den and the old hyena called out: "Ho, Lion! I want to talk to you."

There was a moment's silence; and then from inside, the lion, who had apparently been sleeping off the effects

of his feast, let out a great roar. He walked slowly out of his den and looked down at the hyena. His great mane stood up, and he was a picture of sheer power in the bright moonlight.

"Well, Friend Hyena?" he asked softly. "Do you want something?"

The old hyena gulped, cleared his throat and picked up the guinea. "Why, Friend Lion," he said meekly, "my sons have told me how you shared your food with them. You were much too generous. We have come to present you with the tenth guinea."

KNOW YOUR OWN STRENGTH

On a farm near the Awash River there lived a donkey and a rooster who were great friends. Now this might seem to you a strange friendship, but there were good reasons for it. The donkey was a meek little fellow who had carried heavy loads all of his life. He had been worked so hard that he had never had a chance to drowse in the sun and talk, which he dearly loved to do. Now that he was old and not used so much for packing things to market, his greatest pleasure was to walk lazily in the sunny meadow, occasionally pluck some tender grass, and talk about all manner of things, such as what makes the stars shine, why some sticks are straight and others crooked, and why there is so much sand in the desert.

Although the rooster did not know much about these weighty subjects, he had a good voice and enjoyed answering the donkey at great length. The donkey seemed to admire his rooster friend's knowledge very much. More important, the rooster was a lazy sort of fellow, and during these long talks in the meadow he rode on the donkey's back — which the donkey did not mind at all since he had carried much heavier loads all his life. Whenever the rooster spied a fat worm or a tasty bug, he would flap down, gobble it up, and then fly again to the donkey's back. Thus he managed to stay well fed all the time, without having to do all the walking around that most roosters and chickens had to do.

All in all it was a pleasant arrangement, and there never were two closer friends anywhere — until the day they met the lion. It was evening. They had fallen into a deep discussion about why water is always wet, and they had not noticed the setting sun.

From a nearby clump of bushes, the lion had been watching the donkey for some time. When the donkey came close, the lion slipped from the bushes and padded silently toward him. The donkey was so frightened that he stopped and stood frozen, unable to lift so much as one foot. The lion was almost on him when for the first time he saw the rooster riding on the donkey's back. The rooster saw the lion at the same moment and crowed in terror and flapped his wings.

Instantly, the lion whirled around and ran back into the bushes. He knew that if the rooster kept crowing and flapping his wings, the farmer in the nearby house would hear him and come running with his gun. The old lion was much too smart to risk getting shot, just for a meal of one skinny donkey.

When the lion disappeared, the donkey slowly got over his fright, and then he became quite amazed. "Did you see that lion run away!" he said to the rooster. "I just stood here bravely and he became afraid of me. What do you know about that!"

The rooster was not quite so sure. "Do you really think he was afraid of you?" he asked doubtfully.

The donkey became very angry at his friend's doubts. He shook the rooster off his back. "Look," he said, "I don't think you'd better ride on me any more, and I'm afraid I won't have any time to talk to you after this. I've got more important things to do than talk. I've got to guard this farm for my master."

The rooster was very sorry to lose his good friend and walked sadly back to the farmyard by himself. All the next day, the donkey went around the farm telling the different animals how the lion had been afraid of him. Toward evening, after having told his story at least fifty times, the donkey trotted off toward the bushes at the edge of the meadow. He thought it was about time to frighten the lion again.

The lion was waiting for him, and this time he made sure that there was no rooster on the donkey's back. He crept out of the bushes, making not a sound but coming forward with a deadly purpose. The donkey snorted and kicked up his heels, but the lion only came faster toward him.

"Listen," said the donkey, "I'm the same brave donkey who was here last night. You'd better get away."

The lion did not answer but instead kept on coming. When the lion was almost on him, the donkey realized that something had gone wrong. He turned tail and ran with all his speed for the farmyard; but while he was a pretty good runner, he was no match for the lion. The lion sprang at him and that would have been the end, except for a very lucky thing. At that moment the donkey stepped in a hole and went sprawling on the ground, turning head over heels. The lion sailed right over him without so much as touching him.

The donkey finished his somersault on his feet and kept right on running without missing a single step. The lion, however, instead of landing on the donkey as he had expected to do, landed on a big rock and the breath was

completely knocked out of him. By the time he got up
and felt like running, the donkey was all the way back
to the farmyard.

The rooster had been perched in a tree and had seen
everything that had happened. As the donkey walked to
the tree and lay down wearily, the rooster fluttered down
on his back. The rooster was really very glad to have
his friend back, but he couldn't help saying something
just a little bit mean.

The rooster said, "Well, my friend, I think we had
better talk about how important it is not to think that
you are stronger than you really are."

The donkey nodded and closed his eyes. He was very,
very tired.

"Yes," he said, "I agree. But let's talk about it tomorrow. And you might be thinking about why lemons
are yellow. We'll talk about that, too."

Whenever we worked or traveled among the Danakil,
we wore guns. Not that we planned to start trouble. We
wore the guns in order to avoid trouble. Among the
Danakil the gun is a symbol of manhood. If a man does
not wear or carry a gun, the Danakil may wonder whether
he is a man at all. In order to test the unarmed visitor,
the Danakil will sometimes jostle him or push him or do
something to start a quarrel.

Once an armed Danakil sat around our campfire out on
the desert and continually spat toward our meal that was
cooking on the fire. We told him to stop, but instead he
directed his aim closer to our supper kettle. In an outer

ring, away from the fire, ten Danakil warriors squatted with their weapons and laughed at the funny fellow who was bothering our cook. We wore no weapons, and our rifles and pistols were in the Land Rover.

Instead of hitting the man or dragging him away from our cook fire, we brought out our weapons. The next time the man spat, one of us fired a shot between his bare feet. He jumped up and joined his friends in the outer circle. But the strange thing was that the Danakil were pleased, rather than angry. We had no further trouble with them, and they even helped drag in wood for the fire. It is rare indeed when a Danakil man will soil his hands with any kind of work.

A police major who had worked long among the Danakil told us a story that is worth retelling. It is a true story, not a folk story.

THE FIGHT WITH CRAZY MAN

A FEW years ago a Somali chief called Crazy Man crossed into Danakil country beyond the Awash River. Crazy Man and his armed followers pushed closer and closer to the river. Behind Crazy Man came the Somali women and children and old men, who began to pasture their goats on the land of the Danakil.

The Danakil were delighted with this challenge to a fight. They let Crazy Man come in further toward the Awash. Meanwhile they sent back to Dessye and Addis for ammunition and guns. When the police heard of this they sent me with a party of policemen into the country

near the Awash. We had had no big trouble in this
country for many years.

The chief of the Danakil at that time was the Fetorari
of Asaita, the man you talked to this evening — the man
who has given you this house to sleep in and this goat's
milk to drink. Now the Fetorari was troubled. On the one
hand, he loved to fight, and he wished to protect his
lands near the river. On the other hand, he is a loyal
Ethiopian, and it is his job to keep the peace in this
country for our Emperor. So he decided that he would
arm his warriors but fire no shots until Crazy Man
crossed the Awash.

I also had troubles then. I could not stop a war that
had not started. Crazy Man would not talk to our mes-
sengers. The Fetorari said, truthfully, that he had not
fired a shot. Meanwhile the goats of the Somali ate the

grass closer to the Awash, and the village people crowded Crazy Man toward the river. I sent back for more policemen.

In order to stop the trouble we placed our line of policemen along the first ridge on this side of the river. The Fetorari was angry because he wished this place for his men. But he set his men up on the second ridge beyond the river. And we waited.

One night, a month after the rains had ended, Crazy Man crossed the river and set up his camp in a valley between our two ridges. The men of the Fetorari began to call out to us, "Go back to Amhara country. We will fight our own wars here."

We called back to them, "If you fire one shot we will hang all of you."

We then called down to Crazy Man, "Go back across the river. We are on both sides of you." Our only answer was a laugh from Crazy Man.

Then we sent word to the Fetorari: "Do not fire one shot, or the army will deal with you."

An hour later the Somali down in the valley opened fire. We fired back, and we killed or wounded every one of them. The Danakil did not fire one shot. The Somali were driven back across the river and out of Danakil country."

When the police major had finished we said, "He was well named — Crazy Man — opening fire in such a place."

"Ah, he was not so stupid," the policeman told us. "He hoped to get the Danakil firing at the police and the police firing at the Danakil. Then he would pull back out of the valley while they fought. But the Danakil did not fire."

One of us said, "I suppose the Danakil were grateful to you for saving their lands."

The policeman laughed. "They hated us all the more after that. We had cheated them out of their greatest pleasure — fighting and killing. I think they have never forgiven me for that."

FIVE

The Gallas:
Mounted Warriors of High Africa

ABOUT three hundred years ago a great human wave washed over the highlands of Ethiopia and it has never receded. The people who formed this wave called themselves *Ilm Orma*, which means the Sons of Men, and they were looking for room to live. The Ethiopians of that day fought these invaders — whom they gave the name of Gallas — and tried to drive them back to the lowlands from which they came. But the Gallas were fierce fighters and there were great numbers of them. They not only stayed in Ethiopia but became the most widespread tribe in the country. Although most of the Gallas live in central and western Ethiopia, every province has large numbers of these people.

The Gallas are the largest tribe of Ethiopia, and of all Africa. Their total number is estimated at six million; but many of them live in Kenya — the country just south of

Ethiopia — from which they originally came. They had to
have living space and they first moved north and east
through the Somali country. Then they came over the
great escarpment that divides highland Ethiopia from
the Danakil desert, and they learned to live in this country that is much higher and colder than their original
home. They have become known as the Northern Gallas,
and they live mostly by farming. Their fellow tribesmen
who stayed in the lower country to the south are called the
Southern Gallas, and they raise cattle for a living. Some of
them live the same way the Somalis and the Danakil do.
They are nomads who move from place to place with their
herds and flocks, ever seeking grass and water.

For many years there was bitter war between the highland tribes and the Galla invaders. Although the Gallas
were good fighters, it became necessary for them to de-
velop a new weapon. This weapon was the horse. They
got their first horses from the Arabs who were also invading Ethiopia at this time. Later they raised their own.
They learned to ride well, and with shield and spear they
became deadly warriors on horseback.

The horsemanship of the Gallas enabled them to keep
their place in high Africa, and it later helped to save the
country. Toward the end of the nineteenth century, Italy,
seeking African colonies, invaded Ethiopia. The Gallas
joined the great Ethiopian Emperor Menelik II and became his cavalry. In the Battle of Aduwa in 1896, the
Gallas fought beside other Ethiopian tribes and helped
to inflict a crushing defeat on the Italians. It was this vic-

tory over a modern European army that made the rest of the world realize Ethiopia was a true country and not just a collection of uncivilized tribes. Thus, at a time when European countries were carving up Africa to make colonies for themselves, Ethiopia was able to keep its independence.

Galla horsemen do not ride in wars against other tribes any more, but on holidays they love to dress themselves and their horses in brilliant colors and have mock battles and contests of riding and fighting skill.

Thousands of Gallas still own horses. When the son of Emperor Haile Selassie was killed in an automobile accident, it was a moving sight to see the long line of Galla horsemen coming silently into the capital city to mourn the dead prince.

Although many Gallas are Christians and others are Moslems, great numbers of them still hold pagan beliefs. They believe in werewolves, in the evil eye, and in the magic of Kalitcha, or wizards. "Devil killing" makes it difficult to drive in some Galla areas of Ethiopia. To kill his devil, a Galla will run across the road just at the moment a car passes. He tries to miss the car's bumper by as few inches as possible so that the car will run over and kill the evil spirit which is always trailing just behind him.

Tree worship, common among the Gallas of western Ethiopia, is also found in other parts of the country. Near Addis Ababa there stands a magnificent wild fig tree with great leafy limbs and a trunk more than twenty feet around. Until recently this was worshiped by Gallas in the area and sacrifices were made to a huge snake which they believed lived inside of it. (One common Galla belief is that the human race was created by a snake.)

But things change even in this ancient land. Today this tree has become an outdoor school, and young Gallas are learning to read and write in the shade of its deep green leaves! This change was brought about by one hard-working young member of the Ministry of Education in Addis Ababa.

Today, as farmers and cattle raisers, the Gallas lead simple, easy lives and refuse to take things too seriously. Most of their stories have a touch of comedy in them, and they love nonsense stories such as this one:

FOUR GOOD MEN

ONE night four men were walking down the road together, and they were a most unusual group. One of the men was blind and had to be led by another, who happened to be stone deaf. The third man was so badly crippled that he had to hobble along on crutches, and the fourth shivered in the cold night wind because he had only a few miserable rags to wear. As they passed near a forest, a scream rang out.

"Listen," said the deaf man, "I heard a scream. Someone must be in trouble."

"Yes," said the blind man, staring into the darkness. "I can see them over there."

"Let's run over and help them," said the crippled man.

"Oh, no," said the man dressed in rags. "They might be robbers and steal all of our clothes!"

But sometimes the Galla jokes are so subtle that you have to think twice to get the point. Here is one of that kind:

One morning two bright young students were on their way to school when they saw an old woman driving a bunch of donkeys down the street. They decided to poke some fun at her.

"Good morning, Mother of Donkeys," one of the students said politely.

The old woman looked at them and answered just as politely, "Good morning, my children."

The Gallas' favorite kind of comedy, however, is the kind that is known in America as "slapstick." It is comedy that gets its laughs from ridiculous situations and actions. A good example is the story of the brave prince, one of the most popular of all the stories of High Africa.

THE BRAVE PRINCE

ONCE upon a time, in the land where the Blue Nile divides the provinces of Shoa and Gojjam, there lived a young prince who was the sorrow of the king's life. The prince was big and handsome, a fast talker, and a clever thinker. It would seem that he was just the man to replace his father as king someday, except for one thing —

and, oh, what a sad thing. The young prince was a coward.

The mere sight of a spear frightened him; the mention of war made him tremble; the roar of a lion paralyzed him. This perhaps would not have been so bad, except that his father was a great warrior and hunter and had expected his son to follow in his footsteps. In fact — and the king always laughed bitterly when he thought of this — he had named the prince *Shi-Guday,* which means "Killer of a Thousand." It was the perfect name for a great warrior.

Once a year there was a royal hunt when the king, members of the royal family, and the best hunters in the tribe went out to prove their courage. Shi-Guday had never been on one of these hunts, but this year his father commanded him to go along. Shi-Guday was terrified. He pretended to be sick; he cried out that his leg was hurt; he said that he had lost his spear. But the king sent the witch doctor with medicine, bandaged his leg, and gave him another spear. Then he ordered the young prince to come along on the hunting party.

The hunters entered the deep forest in a group, but soon they spread out, as each searched for the fiercest animal and the biggest prize. All but Shi-Guday, that is. He stayed close to the greatest hunter in the party and hoped that the man would protect him if a lion should suddenly appear. But he was not strong enough to keep up with the great hunter, and before long Shi-Guday found himself crashing along through the underbrush by himself. Not a single member of the hunting party was in sight, and though he shouted name after name, no one answered him. The thought of being alone made him shake with fear and he started running. He must have run in the wrong direction, for after an hour he was in a part of the forest he had never seen before, and he was thoroughly lost. He wandered around crying for help, but a dreadful silence was his only answer.

At last darkness settled over the forest. Though he was so tired he could hardly move, Shi-Guday climbed to the top of a tall tree and wedged himself into a forked branch. He tried to sleep. But the forest came alive with the night sounds of animals and birds, and Shi-Guday was so frightened that he could not even close his eyes.

Suddenly there was such a blood-curdling noise below him that Shi-Guday jumped and slipped right through the forked branch. He landed squarely on top of a great, shaggy monster that howled again and started running. Shi-Guday was so paralyzed that he could not even slip off the beast, and the tighter he held on, the faster the animal ran. All of the time Shi-Guday was crying, "Uuuuuu! Uuuuuu! Uuuuuu!" which was the sound he always made when he was in great fear. But this weird cry only made the beast run harder, and finally he ran all the way through the forest and into another country where a different king ruled.

The beast ran right through the town where the king lived, and all of the people were amazed at the strange sight and at the weird cry that Shi-Guday was making. In the town's light Shi-Guday saw that the monster was in reality a great hyena. Then he was not quite so afraid,

and he loosened his grip and fell to the ground. The people picked up Shi-Guday, who, though quite exhausted,
struck a brave pose and said, "Don't stand there gaping,
you fools. I rode that hyena only because my lion was
lame. I prefer riding the lion. Take me to your king."

Now it so happened that the king's daughter, the Princess Fannay, had been watching from a window and had
seen Shi-Guday ride into town on the hyena's back. She
heard his brave words. With her woman's wisdom, she
knew that Shi-Guday had really been paralyzed with fear,
but nevertheless she fell in love with him at first sight.
For, indeed, he was a handsome man and clearly of royal
birth.

Princess Fannay went to Shi-Guday and said to him,
"When you see the king tell him that 'Uuuuuu' is a war
cry in your country. Say that you usually ride a ferocious
lion. My father admires courage in a man above all else."

Shi-Guday took one look at the Princess Fannay and
decided that he must have her for his bride. When the
guards brought him before the king, Shi-Guday spoke
exactly as the princess had told him to. The king was also
impressed with the fact that Shi-Guday was the crown
prince of a neighboring kingdom, and he made Shi-Guday
welcome in his palace. It was only a little while before
Shi-Guday asked for the king's permission to marry the
Princess Fannay, and the king readily agreed to this match.

Plans for the wedding and feast were almost complete
when word come to the palace that a terrible lion was
ravaging the country — killing cattle and sheep and even
walking boldly into villages to attack children and old

people. The king knew that the wedding could not be celebrated properly until the lion was killed or driven away, so he called Shi-Guday before him.

"It is good that you are here," he said, "for my people have had little experience with lions. A man of your courage, however, will have no trouble in getting rid of this beast. The wedding will take place just as soon as you return from battling this savage creature."

Shi-Guday was so frightened at the king's words that he could not speak. But the king thought that Shi-Guday's silence meant that he thought killing a lion was too unimportant to talk about. The king was much pleased with the courage of his son-in-law to be.

The Princess Fannay understood Shi-Guday's fear, however, and gave him much *tej* to drink, and she loaded a horse with still more of the powerful drink. Now a man who has drunk too much *tej* thinks little of fear, or of anything else for that matter. Shi-Guday climbed on the horse and entered the forest without a worry. The people who watched him ride away marveled at his courage.

After he had ridden for about an hour Shi-Guday became very sleepy. His eyes closed and he tumbled off his horse and lay snoring on the soft grass. The horse, frightened by Shi-Guday's fall, reared up and all of the jars of *tej* fell to the ground and broke. As it happened, however, the *tej* did not soak into the ground but instead trickled into a rock hollow and stayed there.

Toward evening the great lion came wandering along, and since the wind was blowing the other way, he did not smell Shi-Guday. He did smell the *tej*, however, and, being thirsty, drank some of it. It did not taste like water, but it tasted good, so he drank all of it. After the lion finished the *tej* he too became very sleepy and he lay down and fell into a deep sleep.

About this time, Shi-Guday woke up, and when he saw that it was almost dark, he decided that he had better get back to the palace as fast as he could. He was still sleepy and a little groggy from the *tej*, however, and he climbed astride the big lion, thinking all the time that it was his horse.

The lion awakened and jumped up with a roar, for it could not imagine what was happening. The lion, still full of *tej*, became very confused and started running. And Shi-Guday, now aware that he was on the back of the lion, gripped his mane and hung on desperately, all the time crying, "Uuuuuu! Uuuuuu! Uuuuuu!"

The lion was so muddled that it did not know or care where it was running. It burst right out of the forest and onto the main street of the king's town, just as the hyena had done a short time before. And so for the second time Shi-Guday entered the town riding a savage animal and crying "Uuuuuu! Uuuuuu!" This time the people could scarcely believe their eyes, for a lion is much more dangerous than a hyena. And this was the biggest and wildest lion that anyone had ever seen.

The lion was so exhausted from the load on its back and the load of *tej* in its stomach that it fell senseless in the middle of the street. The lion was stuffed into a cage, and Shi-Guday was cheered by the people and once more taken before the king.

"Perhaps I should have killed the lion," Shi-Guday explained. "But my horse had bolted. I had no other way to get home. It was the poorest riding lion I've ever seen, though."

"Never have I seen such bravery in a man," said the happy king. "The marriage between Shi-Guday and the Princess Fannay must take place tomorrow!"

And so the marriage took place, and the people feasted and made merry because the brave prince would some

day be their king. Everyone was happy for many months,
but suddenly one day the happiness ended. A savage tribe
that lived to the south invaded the peaceful land. These
cruel invaders burned houses and stole the cattle and
grain of the farmers. In two days' time they were less than
a mile from the city of the king.

The old king called Shi-Guday before him and said,
"My son, you are our only hope. You must lead my soldiers against these savage people. With a great warrior
like you to lead them, my men will fight bravely."

The king had the wildest and most powerful horse in
the kingdom brought around for Shi-Guday to ride. Just
the sight of this great animal sent chills of fear up the
prince's spine, and the thought of riding him into war
frightened him so that he was unable to move a muscle.
The Princess Fannay, who knew her husband very well,
called two servants and said to them:

"Lift Prince Shi-Guday onto his horse. He wants to
save every bit of his energy for fighting the enemy. The
prince wants you to tie his legs together so that no matter
how many times he is hit by the savages and no matter
how hard, he cannot be knocked off his horse."

And so, almost fainting, Shi-Guday was lifted onto the
horse and his legs were tied tightly together around the
horse's belly. Then the king himself gave the horse a
smart slap on the flank, and the great animal went charging down the road in the direction of the invading army.
The king's soldiers followed and took courage from the
cries of "Uuuuuu! Uuuuuu! Uuuuuu!" that rang out
from Shi-Guday. They thought that this was his battle cry

and they took it up and rode toward the enemy shouting "Uuuuuu! Uuuuuu!"

When Shi-Guday caught sight of the savages with their
gleaming spears, he reached desperately for the branch
of a small tree to try to stop his charging horse. The
horse was going so fast, however, and Shi-Guday clung so
tightly to the branch, that the tree was pulled up by its
roots without so much as slowing the horse! Shi-Guday
reached for another tree and the same thing happened.
And this happened again and again. The horse charged
on at the enemy with Shi-Guday uprooting tree after
tree.

The savages had never in their lives seen anything like
this — a big man on a big horse bearing down on them
shouting, "Uuuuuu! Uuuuuu! Uuuuuu!" and uprooting
trees as he came. And behind him, two lines of the king's
soldiers waving their spears bravely and making the
strange cry of "Uuuuuu! Uuuuuu!" The savages in front
of Shi-Guday threw down their spears and ran for their
lives into the deep forest. Their running spread panic
through the other invaders, and before Shi-Guday had
even reached them, the battle was over. The king's soldiers chased the savages all the way out of the country
and took back all of the cattle and grain they had stolen.

Shi-Guday became the greatest hero that the country
had ever known. And when the old king died not long
after the great victory over the savages, Shi-Guday took
his place as ruler. Since he was generous and friendly, he
made a good king for the people.

One day Shi-Guday went to the queen Fannay and said,

"I have been thinking, my good wife. Now that I am king, I owe it to my people not to take any more risks. Therefore we will hire brave soldiers — like myself — from my father's country to fight for the king, in case it is necessary."

And Queen Fannay, who loved Shi-Guday very much, answered, "I am sure your idea is a good one, my dear husband. The people would die of grief if anything should happen to their brave king."

A MOST GENEROUS HOST

"You ask me if the Amharas are good people!" The old Galla storyteller smiled. "Oh, yes, my children. They are fine people and so very kind and generous. Surely you know the story of the poor Galla traveler who asked help from the Amhara farmer, Aba Bidaru. You do not know this story? Well, fill my cup once more with coffee and I will tell it to you. Then you will never need to ask again if the Amharas are good people . . ."

The traveler's name was Gugsa, and he had walked into Gojjam to buy a bull. It cost him most of the money he had, and it was not a very good bull. Still, it was the best he could afford and he was very proud of it. He was on his way home when darkness overtook him. He had wanted to reach the next village before stopping; but he was afraid that a lion might scent his bull and attack. So he stopped at the first farmhouse he came to.

It happened that this was the house of Aba Bidaru, an

Amhara. Aba Bidaru opened the door and saw a Galla leading a good bull. Aba Bidaru smiled.

"I seek shelter for the night," Gugsa said. "I fear that lions will attack my bull."

"Of course, you are welcome to spend the night," said Aba Bidaru. "Come in and my wife will prepare supper for you. And while you are eating, I will take your bull to the stream to drink."

Gugsa was warmed by this kindness and he stepped into the house with many thanks. Aba Bidaru led away the bull, and Gugsa sat down at the table to eat. He did not eat much because he didn't want to seem greedy when Aba Bidaru was being so very kind to him.

Just as he was finishing his meal, Gugsa heard a great shouting and crying outside, and Aba Bidaru burst into the house.

"Oh! Oh! Oh!" he wailed, rolling his eyes. "Your poor bull! Just as he was beginning to drink at the stream, a huge male lion pounced on him. Then the female joined in, and the two lions dragged the bull away. There was nothing I could do to stop them."

Gugsa leaped from his chair and ran outside. He grabbed his spear and hurried toward the stream. "Show me the exact spot where my bull was attacked," he called to Aba Bidaru.

Aba Bidaru led Gugsa to a place where the stream narrowed and pointed to the nearby bushes which grew thickly. "The lions came from there," he said, "and dragged the bull back in there."

Gugsa went over to look and saw that the bushes had

been disturbed. He crept cautiously in, but the night was
dark and he could see nothing. Now Gugsa was no coward, but he knew that if two lions were in there, it would
be foolish to hunt them in the darkness. They would
surely see him first and kill him. Besides, his bull would
long since have been killed.

Gugsa walked sadly back to the house. Aba Bidaru
walked beside him, telling Gugsa how sorry he was about
what had happened. When they reached the house Aba
Bidaru took Gugsa to a pen where there was a fine fat
goat.

"Look," said Aba Bidaru, "I feel at fault because your
bull was killed. I want you to take this fine goat in its
place."

Now the goat was a handsome animal and Gugsa would
have liked very much to have him — even though he was
not worth as much as a bull — but he shook his head.

"No," said Gugsa, "it was not your fault that my bull
was killed. You were only trying to help me."

But Aba Bidaru insisted that his guest should have the
goat. Finally, feeling better about his lost bull, Gugsa
accepted the goat.

Gugsa was very tired from his day's journey, so Aba
Bidaru showed him to the place where he would sleep.
Then Aba Bidaru blew out the light and went to bed
himself.

Sometime deep in the night, Gugsa was awakened by
a great shouting and crying outside. He jumped up from
his mat, groped his way to the door, and ran out into the

night. Aba Bidaru was standing there with a torch in one hand and a sack in the other. He was wailing most terribly.

"Oh, your poor goat!" cried Aba Bidaru, when he saw Gugsa. "I heard a noise in the pen and went outside to look. I found that thieves had stolen the goat. I chased them bravely, but could not catch them. However, I got so close to them that I frightened them, and they dropped this sack. It contains two gourds of good butter. Since you have lost your goat, I want you to take this butter."

Gugsa was very sad at losing his fine goat, but he thanked Aba Bidaru for the butter. He took it into the house and put it on a table. Then he took his spear and went out into the night to look for the thieves who had stolen his goat. He searched for many hours in the direction which Aba Bidaru had chased the thieves. He could find no trace of them. At last, very unhappy, he returned to Aba Bidaru's house and went to bed. Two gourds of butter was poor exchange for his fine fat goat, but still it was better than nothing. Gugsa felt that Aba Bidaru was very generous to give him the butter that the thieves had dropped.

Gugsa went back to sleep, but he was awakened early the next morning by a great arguing between Aba Bidaru and his wife. Gugsa got up sleepily and went to see what the trouble was.

"Oh, Gugsa," cried Aba Bidaru. "Do you know what this stupid woman has done? She has used your butter to make the *wot*. Now we have no other butter to give you in exchange. But I will fill your water container with good hot coffee for your journey."

Since Aba Bidaru had given him the butter out of kindness in the first place, Gugsa could not complain about getting coffee in exchange for it. So Aba Bidaru's wife filled Gugsa's water gourd with coffee. Gugsa set it outside the door of the house while he went to make one last search for his bull and his goat.

He searched again for many hours but found not a trace of either bull or goat. He decided that hyenas must have finished whatever bits of the bull that the lions had left. When he returned to the house, he found Aba Bidaru sitting outside his door. Aba Bidaru held Gugsa's water gourd in his hands and he looked sad.

"Oh, Gugsa," he said, "a very bad thing has happened. One of my little children found the gourd of coffee that you left outside the door, and he drank all of it. Now he is very sick. I must take him to the doctor."

Gugsa was sorry to hear this. He felt that it was his fault, since he had left the coffee where the little child could get it. "I am very sorry," Gugsa said. "Is there anything I can do?"

Aba Bidaru shook his head mournfully. "No," he said. "And I do not know what I shall do. I have no money to pay the doctor."

Now Gugsa had a little money left. Though he would go hungry if he gave it away, he said to Aba Bidaru, "I have a little money. Use it to pay the doctor."

Aba Bidaru brightened at once. "You are a very good

man to offer your money," he said. "Two dollars will be enough to pay the doctor."

Two dollars happened to be all the money that Gugsa had, but he did not hesitate to hand it over to Aba Bidaru.

And then Gugsa went on his way, sorry that he had lost his bull, and his goat, and his butter, and his coffee, and the little bit of money he had. But he was sorrier still that he had caused the good Amhara farmer Aba Bidaru so much trouble.

One of the commonest forms of folk stories told in high Africa is the story which deals with a trial and a judgment. The main character in such stories is usually a judge or a king. Sometimes the judge or king is shown to be a wise man, but more often than not he is made to appear stupid or foolish. There is a good reason for this. The highland African kings have always ruled the people with a stern hand. At certain periods in the past, these kings have been cruel, and the people have been afraid to protest openly against their actions. An old Ethiopian proverb says, "The sky cannot be plowed nor a king questioned." In other words, it is as foolish to speak out against the things a king does, as it is to try to farm in the clouds.

But one safe way that the people could protest against injustice was through stories about kings and judges. These stories changed the names and places and poked fun at the king and his judges. Judges appeared in these stories because they were appointed by the king. Often, all the characters in the stories were disguised as different animals.

The two stories which follow are typical of high African justice folk tales. The first one about the judge is pure comedy and fun. The judge is not treated harshly, even though he is made to seem foolish. But you can well imagine the hatred that the people must have had for the real king who inspired the second story, the tale of King Firdy the Just.

THE WISE JUDGE

THE good widow Yemswitch, who many years ago had lost most of her hearing, had now lost all of her sheep. The whole flock had wandered off while she was washing clothes at the river, and she had not the least idea where they had gone. She set out looking for them and soon met the good farmer Mulugeta, who had just finished his day's plowing.

"Ato Mulugeta," said Yemswitch, "have you seen my sheep anywhere today?"

Now it so happened that Mulugeta was also hard of hearing; if anything, deafer than Yemswitch. He always had to guess at what a person was saying. Since he had just come from his field, he guessed that the good widow was asking about his work.

"Yes, Wizero Yemswitch," he answered, "I have worked very hard today."

He pointed toward his plowed field to show her how much he had done. Yemswitch, however, did not hear a word that he said. She thought that he was pointing in the direction that he had seen her sheep going.

"Thank you, Farmer Mulugeta," she said. "If I find my sheep over there, I shall give you one of them."

They bowed politely to each other, and Yemswitch went looking for her sheep in the direction that Mulugeta had pointed. As luck would have it, she found the sheep in a little grove of trees just over the hill. She was very grateful to the good farmer for having been so careful to watch which way her sheep were going. Had she not found them before dark, the jackals or leopards certainly would have got them.

Yemswitch discovered that one of the lambs had a badly injured leg, and she decided to give this lamb to Mulugeta. She went to his house and found him preparing his own supper, for his wife had been dead for many years.

"Ato Mulugeta," Yemswitch said, "I found my sheep exactly where you said they were. I have brought you this fine lamb for a reward."

Mulugeta heard nothing that she said, but he saw that the lamb had an injured leg. He thought that Yemswitch was accusing him of hurting the lamb.

"Oh, no," he said firmly. "I had nothing to do with that. Why should I hurt your lamb?"

Yemswitch, who heard clearly only the word "no," thought that Mulugeta wanted a better sheep for his

reward. "You are a greedy man," she said. "All you did
was point the direction. Here, take this lamb or none at
all."

She tried to put the lamb in his arms, but he refused to
take it. "I will not pay for this lamb," he said. "I had
nothing to do with its accident."

They fell to arguing, abusing each other, and calling
names. But of course this made little difference since
neither of them heard one-tenth of what the other said.
They made so much noise, however, that a policeman
heard them and insisted that they go to a judge to settle
their quarrel.

They went to the court of Justice Yasu Wolde-Johannas, an old and wise judge who was famous throughout the land for the fairness of his court decisions. It
might seem strange that Justice Yasu could be so wise
and fair in deciding cases that were brought before him.
The truth was that he could scarcely hear a word that
was said, even when shouted. But the good man was also
nearly blind and so he could not judge people on how
they looked, as almost everyone does. This made him a
very fair judge.

The widow Yemswitch told her side of the case first.
She pointed to the lamb which she still held. "My reward
was generous. Ato Mulugeta is a greedy man to want
more."

Mulugeta then explained at great length that he was a
kind man who would never think of hurting a little
lamb. "I was busy in my field all day," he said. "I had
not even seen the animal until she accused me."

Judge Yasu listened carefully, though he heard nothing, and peered intently at the two people before him. Finally he made out that they were an old man and an old woman. The woman, he decided, was holding a child in her arms. The judge had had much experience with the troubles of people. He decided that this man and woman wanted to get a divorce. They wanted him to decide which one should keep the child.

"How many years have you been married?" the judge asked.

Yemswitch, listening carefully, thought that the judge had asked her how many sheep she had.

"Twenty, Your Worship," she shouted at the top of her voice.

The judge heard this answer, and he at once reached his decision. "I am ashamed of you both," he said. "You have been married for twenty years and still have not learned to live together. My decision is that you must continue to live together and to make a good home for this little child. And if you do not do this, I shall put you both in prison. That is all. The case is dismissed."

The officers of the court finally made Yemswitch and Mulugeta understand the decision of Judge Yasu.

"But how can we live together?" wailed Yemswitch. "We are not married."

"Then you had better get married," the bailiff told her. "The good judge will surely put you into prison if you do not carry out his order."

And so the widow Yemswitch and the farmer Mulugeta went to a priest and were married that night.

Since Yemswitch was a very good cook and Mulugeta was a very good farmer — and since neither of them could ever hear what the other was saying — they lived happily ever afterward.

And the fame of the wise Judge Yasu Wolde-Johannas spread even further through the land.

KING FIRDY THE JUST

In the western lands of high Africa there once lived a great king known as King Firdy the Just. He prided himself on the fairness with which he judged the cases that were brought before him. No one in the country had ever been heard to say a word against the decisions that King Firdy reached. This was a good thing because the king had long ago decreed that anyone who spoke against him should be roasted over a slow fire.

One night in the king's city a thief named Asrat tried to break into the home of a wealthy merchant by digging a hole through a wall of the man's house. Just when the hole was big enough, however, a brick fell out of the wall and hit Asrat on the head. It was really a nasty blow, and the thief had to stagger away with only a bloody head and a big bump for his night's work.

Asrat was very angry at what had happened, and the next morning he went to the palace of King Firdy the Just to complain. "Last night, O King," he said, "I was breaking into the house of the merchant Paulos to steal a few trifling things. But a brick fell out of the wall and hit me on the head. Look, you can still see the bump. I was too badly hurt to continue my work. Someone should be punished for this."

King Firdy looked at the bump, and his voice shook with rage when he spoke, "You are right! What has this country come to when a thief cannot break into a house without risking accidents of this kind?" The king turned to his guards and said, "Bring the merchant Paulos to me."

The merchant was brought and he trembled with fear. Everyone stood in terror of the justice of King Firdy. "Merchant," said the king, "this good thief was injured while trying to break into your house. Since it was your house, it is my judgment that you are to blame."

"Oh, King," said the merchant in a quaking voice, "it is true that it was my house. But the person to blame is really the carpenter who built the house for me. He must have built the house badly. That is why the brick fell."

"Perhaps you are right," said the king. "Bring the carpenter to me. My only desire is to punish the guilty person."

The carpenter was brought before King Firdy. The king said, "You wretched man! Do you know that the good thief Asrat has been injured because of careless work you did on the house of the merchant Paulos? A brick fell and struck poor Asrat on the head while he was digging through the wall."

The carpenter was nearly fainting from fear, but he managed to say, "Oh, King, it is true that I built the

house. But the bricks were put in by the stonemason
Felleke. It is he who should be punished."

"Bring the stonemason Felleke to me," said King Firdy,
"and I will see that justice is done."

So the stonemason was brought before King Firdy.
When the king accused him of causing the injury to the
thief Asrat, Felleke whispered in terror, "Oh, good King,
it is not I who should be punished for the injury to the
thief. The man who sold me the mortar to hold the
bricks together was Kebede Gabre. If the mortar had
been good, the brick would not have fallen on the thief's
head. It is Kebede who should be punished."

Kebede was brought before the king and the king said,
"Hear, you wretched man! You who made the mortar
that held together the bricks that were used to build the
house of the merchant Paulos. While trying to steal a few
trifling things, the good thief Asrat was struck on the
head by one of these bricks. The brick must have come
loose because of poor mortar. You shall be punished se-
verely for this."

Unfortunately, Kebede was a huge oaf of a man who
had great strength but little brain. He could think of
nothing to say in his defense. King Firdy — sure that he
had found the guilty man — commanded that a gallows
be built and that the man Kebede be hanged at once.

The carpenters built the gallows hastily, however, and
they did not build it high enough. Kebede was an extremely tall man. The guards took him to the gallows to
hang him, but they found that when the rope was around
his neck his feet still touched the ground.

The guards reported this problem to King Firdy the Just, and the king was terribly angry. "How much longer is the wrong that was done to the good thief Asrat to go unpunished?" he shouted. "A gallows has been built and someone must be punished. Find someone who will fit the gallows and hang him!"

So the guards went out, and the first man they met was a little onion farmer who had just come to town to sell his crop. It was well known that this little farmer was a good man who had never harmed anyone. But he was small and so would fit the gallows perfectly. King Firdy was inside his palace crying for justice.

When the farmer was taken before Firdy, the king shouted, "Yes! Yes! Do not bother me with details. He will do perfectly. The good thief has waited long enough for justice. On with the execution!"

So the little onion farmer was taken to the gallows. He fitted it very well, and justice was done in the land of King Firdy.

Do you think it is strange to find in the fourth grade a man who is thirty years old? This story is about such a man. It is not a folk story. It is a true story of modern Africa. In a village of Ethiopia, in a fourth-grade class, we found this man. He sat among the little children; he recited the lessons as they did. He sang the songs and read the books that they did. But he was old enough to be the father of the children with whom he sat. He sat among the children, with his knees hunched up to his

chin; and he looked very serious as he read the story of
Heidi. After the class we talked to him, and he told us this
story.

THE LONG WALK

Do not laugh. I am happy here, learning. I began to walk
toward this place fifteen years ago. And it has been a
long journey.

I was perhaps fifteen when I started out. I am not
sure how old I was. I lived in a village in western Ethiopia. In such villages the old ones do not always know the
ages of children.

At the time, wonderful tales came to our village. They
said that the Italians had gone from the country. They
said that in Addis Ababa our Emperor had made schools
for us all. I too wished to go to school. I went out from
my village toward Addis Ababa. There was a merchant
traveling to Addis, and I worked for him, driving his
mules.

I did good work for that merchant, and he came to
love me as his son. But at night, when we shared our
food, he talked against schools. He said that learning had
not helped him grow rich. "No book," he said, "is as
beautiful as the green hills around Gimbi. No book can
be a wife, or a mother, or a brother to you. You can love
books but they cannot love you." I did not argue with
him. If I argued, I got no bread in the night.

When we reached Addis I ran away from that man, the merchant. I took no money from him. I did not want to argue more about books or school. I wandered in the market. Some people joked at me. I was a wild boy. I had only rags to wear. I did not speak the language of the Amharas. I was afraid and sick. In the day I hid in the grain market behind the sacks. In the night I took food away from the hyena.

But one day a man from my village found me. He was a friend of my father's. The man gave me food and a place to sleep, and I worked for him. The man cut trees and we burned them and made charcoal to sell to the people. This man was like my father to me. I spoke to him of the school, but he became angry. "What is the need for school? God made us wise or foolish. Other men cannot change the work of God."

Near the wood yard there was a priest's school. When the man went to the forest I walked near the priest's school. I stood there and watched, and in that way I learned much of the Amharic letters. I learned all the letters of the alphabet. I read through the *Abu Gida,* but I did not go to *Wongel.* The woodcutter was a kind man. He gave me some money for clothes. I found papers on the road and tried to read the letters. I saved my money. The woodcutter had many daughters and no sons. He wished me to marry one of his daughters. I ran away from his house with my money.

I worked as a servant boy for a policeman. One day he found me reading my papers. I told him of school. "That is good," he said. "A man who cannot read cannot call himself a man. All animals make sounds. Only man can read them."

This policeman found me a place in the mission school. In the school compound I chopped wood for the fires. I brought water to the kitchens. Since I slept outside the gate at night, I began to cough very much. The doctor of the mission said I was sick. He said I must stop work and stop studying. He brought me to the hospital. I did not like that place, and I ran away to my friend the policeman.

My friend got me into police cadet school. I learned how to read letters and words, and I learned some writing in the police school. I took the policeman's name. He was an Amhara man. But in the school they knew I was a Galla boy. They made me leave the school one day.

I met a man who was an Englishman. He said it was too bad that I was not in the Sudan. In the Sudan, he said, there were many schools. The schools were free for all boys. I knew that Sudan was west of Nekemti and west of my village. I thought I would go to the Sudan.

I started to walk to the Sudan. Now I know it was hundreds of miles through the jungles and over the desert. But I did not know that then. I knew only the way west to Nekemti and my village.

The way to Nekemti was hard. It was the month of Mayazya, and it was raining in the west. I was always wet. I lost all of my clothes in the river. I began to cough and cough. My legs hurt so much. Ay, what hurt! I can remember the hurt in my legs and near my heart. And a man beat me with a stick outside a *tej* house. When I stopped to ask for food, he beat me and laughed. I did not know how to fight. I have learned that since.

After eight days I came to Nekemti. My neck was swollen big, and I was sick, and I fell on the street. A woman took me to the Swedish mission. They said that I had a broken arm, from that man with the stick. They said I had tuberculosis in the neck. They said my legs were bad. I stayed in bed and they gave me medicine. When I could work, I helped them. I cleaned and put whitewash on walls. I mixed mud to make the walls of a schoolroom. I asked to go to that school, but they would not let me. They said I was a stupid boy. They were right. I was a very stupid boy then. So I left the Swedish mission.

I walked west from Nekemti toward Sudan. Beyond Nekemti is the Didessa River where the Shankilla people live. They are wild men. At night, when I slept at the ford called Janno, those people came. They stole my clothes and cut my legs. At another ford there were policemen and they helped me. I walked on toward Gimbi. But almost I couldn't walk. The cut on my leg grew big. I put leaves on it, and some paper, but it did not get better.

In Gimbi there was a mission. I worked for the doctor there. He was a very kind man. He healed the wound on my leg. I needed clothes for my journey, and so I stole the coat and pants of that doctor. I walked through the night and the next day I was near Neggio, and beyond Dilla. I walked back from there to Gimbi, the next day and night. I returned to the doctor his coat and pants. He gave me some of his old clothes. Sometimes I stole things, but not from kind men.

In two days and nights I was at my village, between Neggio and Mundi. My family were so glad to see me. They thought I had come back from Addis a rich man. I had only the old coat of the priest to give to my father. My mother gave me baked corn and honey water, and I walked on.

In Mundi they said I could not cross Dabus, the big river there. "The Dabus is high and full. It is so full. You will sleep down with the crocodiles there."

I walked on from Mundi to the river in two days. I had the corn to eat, and I was strong. When I came to the Dabus, it was night. But I saw it was full. I stayed on the bank in the thick jungle. A Shorgalie village was moving across the Dabus. They are people who live in Ethiopia and the Sudan.

I don't like Shorgalie people, but I stayed that night by their fire near the river. I hid my food in my clothes and said I had no food. They gave me bread. It rained all that night and the next day, and the Dabus came up high on the bank. I sat there looking at the water for two days. It went by my eyes, just gray color and not fast. On the third day the village headman tried to cross. We followed and beat near him in the water to frighten the crocodile. But he could not cross. I was a tall boy and I tried. I was very frightened, but I tried. I think a crocodile tried to take me. I came back to the bank.

The Shorgalie had a gun and they said they would hunt. They said they would give meat to anyone who came out to carry it. I didn't like to eat the meat of wild animals, but I was very hungry then. We hunted through the thick jungle at the river edge, and up in the bamboo thickets. We moved very quietly. We did not want to meet the red buffalo. We were hunting for oryx.

We went beyond the oryx place and made a great noise. We walked toward the men who had the spears. But as we walked, making a great noise, the red buffalo came out. He ran right at us. He ran over another man and me. The other man was killed by the buffalo. I was hurt in the stomach. They carried the dead man and me back to the river bank. And they killed an oryx. The next day the water went down. The Shorgalie crossed the river. They took their dead man, but they left me lying on the river bank.

There was meat left there but I could not eat. I had the fever and I was shaking. I was on the river bank two days. Maybe it was much longer. I could not see up to the sun. It rained and that cooled my fever. At night the animals came in and I threw the meat far from where I lay.

One day a man came on a horse. He said he was going to Asosa. He was a Galla man and he knew of my village. He told me I could go with him on his horse. He said I could not ride, but I could walk and hold on to the horse.

I got very wet crossing the Dabus. Without the horse, I would have drowned there. It rained from Dabus to

Asosa, and sometimes when I slipped the horse hurt me. The kind man with the horse asked me why I wished to travel to Asosa. I did not tell him.

In Asosa that kind man gave me to the police. He said that I was a Sudani who had come into Ethiopia. Maybe the police gave him money. The police took me with them on a patrol to the border near Kurmuk. They told me to cross to the Sudan. I crossed into a village in the Sudan where the police took me. They put me in prison and it was very hot there. In the night the police came to the prison. They said they had no food. They asked me to leave in the night. In that way they got the food for me and kept it for themselves.

I met a Moslem boy on the road, and he said that he was going to Khartoum. He said that his father was a very rich man in Khartoum. He said that I could come to Khartoum and be his slave.

That boy was a very funny boy. He taught me to speak some Arabic. He preached to me of the Koran. And he told everyone he met that I was his slave. He was a little boy and very funny. "He is my slave," the boy shouted in the villages. "I took this one in a war with the Ethiopians." He would dance around me. All the men in the villages would laugh and they would give us food.

That funny boy was not rich. His father's house was not even in Khartoum, but in a poor village. In that village I worked tending goats. I was the slave of the boy. But he taught me Arabic, and he showed me how to make marks on my face. And one night I said to that little boy, "I am tired of being your slave, little boy. I am almost a man, and you are a boy. Good-by." That boy! He screamed. He said, "My people kill slaves." But I walked away from him, and he began to cry.

The trip to Khartoum was terrible. I crossed a great hot place and I nearly died. And when I reached Khartoum I could not go to school. I had no papers. Instead I worked in a British house for almost a year as a houseboy. I learned to clean and press uniforms with a hot iron. I learned to keep rooms clean. I learned to speak English.

One day I went down to the school. I said I was a Sudani. The man there took my name. But he had a policeman follow me to my home. They took me to the police station. They found that I was from Ethiopia. They wanted to send me back. They were sure that I had done some bad thing back in my country. They said, "All Ethiopians are bad."

My English boss came to the police station and promised to send me back to Ethiopia. I knew the head English policeman from my houseboy work. He liked me. The police let me go.

The wife of the Englishman gave me money. She told me to go to Port Sudan. She said that her brother was a merchant there and that he would help me. I did not use her money to ride to Port Sudan on the bus or on a truck. I walked there, and sometimes I rode on a lorry. When I got to her brother's company, they said he was gone away to England on leave. It was then July and very hot in Port Sudan. I think that is the hottest place in the world. The coldest is Korea.

In Port Sudan I worked loading ships. But I got sick
and the fever came so strongly I could not work. The
police found me in the street. Those police were kind
men. A doctor said I was very sick. They put me on a
ship for Massawa, to return me to my country. From
Massawa I went to Asmara. I almost died coming up the
great hills. It was very hot, and the country was filled
with *shifta* (bandits). I was too sick to work in Asmara. An
Italian lady helped me. When I felt better I worked with
her brother who drove a lorry. In that way I came back to
Addis Ababa.

I was sick in Addis for a very long time. I wanted to go
to school. The Italian said that they sent men to school
in the army. I went into the army. I was a few years
down in the Ogaden in the Somali country. Then they
sent us to Korea.

I liked that war over there. The food was very good,
and the clothes were very fine, but there was a noise all
the time. Then one day I was hurt by a bullet. We started
to run up to the top of a hill with an American man. I
don't know what was up there, but it was very high.
When we got almost to the top, the American was lying
in a hole. I asked him something. He was dead. And then
they shot me from somewhere.

Later they brought me back. I was in some very fine
hospitals. I came back to Ethiopia. I could not walk very
well, so they gave me some money. I came back to this
village, and a friend and I bought a half gasha of coffee
land. There is not much to do, and we do not make
much money, but we have enough. So I go to school now.

I would like to be a teacher. A teacher can spend all of his days in a school.

I walked a long time toward this place. I was very lucky and now I am happy here.

SIX

The Guragies:
Workmen of High Africa

GURAGIE country is south and west of Addis Ababa, the capital of Ethiopia. Guragie country is carefully farmed country. It is a land of well-cared-for barley and wheat fields. For the Guragies are the most industrious people of high Africa. They do not hunt as the Borana tribesmen do. They are not great horsemen like the Gallas, or great warriors like the Danakil and Somali men of the desert. The Guragies work, work, work. The word for laborer in high Africa is "Guragie."

The Guragies build the largest huts in Africa. Each Guragie has three houses, built around a compound yard. The Guragie and his cattle live in two of the houses, and in the third house he stores the grain from his carefully tended fields. He stores his wheat and barley and oats, and the banana leaves which he ferments to make his main food, *inset*.

With such comfortable homes, we would expect the Guragie to stay in his compound yard. But the Guragie does leave his home and village to travel all over high Africa. He travels in search of work. Tending herds and plowing fields are not enough for the industrious Guragie. He travels to the ports of Assab and Massawa on the Red Sea to load ships. He works, building high mountain roads in northern Ethiopia. He goes south to Kaffa, the land where coffee first was grown, to work on the farms. The Guragie works hard, saves his money, and returns to his fields and compounds.

We would expect the Guragie to teach his children to work hard and save their money. We would expect the Guragie to think that a man builds things bit by bit. We would expect him to be interested in money and goods, rather than war and magic. The stories we heard in Guragie country are like that. We feel these stories teach the things that the Guragie cares about.

The Guragies are humble. They believe in getting things slowly and by hard work, and they believe in working together.

LIVE ALONE, DIE ALONE

THE lions and the leopards left the mountains and traveled far to the south where the plains were full of fat antelope. Since there was no one left to kill the mountain antelope, the hyenas and the vultures were very hungry. Many of the hyenas settled down to wait for their friends to die. But this took a long time.

One wise old hyena said to his two sons, "A great
tragedy has come upon us. The killer lions and leopards
have left our country. There is no one left in the mountains who can kill for us. We must go to another country."

"But where should we go?" the hyena sons asked.
"Should we follow the leopards and lions to the south?
The way is long and hard. We are too weak now. There
will be strong hyenas and vultures there, and we will get
little food."

"We do not have to travel that far," the hyena said.
"It is true that leopards and lions have left our mountains. But down in the valley there are men. Men kill
more than leopards and lions do. We will go there."

The hyena and his sons traveled through the valley of
men. But a bad thing had come to this country. Men
were not killing there either. The men who killed with
guns had gone south to follow the lions and leopards and
kill them.

After traveling without food through the valley of
men, the hyena and his sons were very weak and hungry.
"It is a terrible thing," the old hyena said. "But we must
become killers. Notice that most of the men have gone
from this place to hunt the lions and leopards. Only
women and children guard the cattle. We will kill a
fat cow."

"But how can we do that?" his sons asked. "We are
not killers."

The oldest hyena son said, "I cannot kill a cow by myself. I am weak with hunger. The cow may step on me

and kill me. He may strike me with his sharp horn or hoof."

"That is true," the old hyena agreed. "One of us cannot kill a cow alone. But there are three of us. Together we can do it."

The hyenas did hunt together. While the smallest hyena talked to the cow, the two big hyenas sneaked around and killed the cow. The three hyenas dragged the cow into the forest and got ready to eat.

But the old hyena drove his sons away from the cow. "This was my idea," he told them. "I am older and bigger and need more food. I will eat all of this cow. You can share the next cow with me."

The two hyena sons were very angry. But they were afraid of their father. They moved away from the cow and sat down and cried.

While the hyena was eating the cow, the owner returned from hunting in the south. The owner began to beat the old hyena with a big stick.

"Help me," the old hyena cried to his sons. "Together we can kill this man. Alone he will kill me. What can I do?"

The young hyenas made no move to help their father. They cried, "Eat alone, die alone!"

The lesson of the first Guragie story is clear. If you don't share your good things, nobody will share your troubles. But somehow we find it a bit cruel. If we had written the story, we would have had the young hyenas change their mind. Perhaps they could have begged for their father's life.

But we didn't write the story. The Guragies did.

GIFT FOR THE LAZY

In a village near Butagira there lived Tesfaye, the lazy man. Tesfaye lived with his father and his brothers. One brother planted and harvested wheat. Another brother grew barley. Tesfaye's father tended a banana grove, cut the leaves, and made *inset* to bury in the storage vaults for winter food. Tesfaye did nothing.

Tesfaye spent his time at the village markets. He went to the Monday market, the Tuesday market, the Thursday market, and the Saturday market. In the market place Tesfaye tried to buy things cheap and sell them for much money. He took the money that his brothers and father earned and bought baskets. But when he tried to sell the baskets, no one wished to buy them. Since it was winter and the time of the great rains, the baskets lay in the market place and were ruined.

Next, Tesfaye tried to raise coffee. But coffee did not grow well near Butagira. Tesfaye brought much wheat to sell, but that year wheat was plentiful, and he could not sell it. Tesfaye always told his family, "One day I will be rich. You will see. You work very hard in the fields. But for little. I will be the rich one."

But Tesfaye did not become rich. Each day his family grew poorer. Tesfaye's brothers had to go away to Addis Ababa to work for money to pay Tesfaye's debts. Tesfaye's father fell sick from worrying and could not tend his bananas. The wheat in the brother's field rotted from the rains. The barley in the fields died. Finally, even Tesfaye knew that he was not growing rich. Instead, he grew poorer.

Tesfaye had one more idea. He thought, "God is good and God is just. I will pray to God to send me money to pay my debts."

Tesfaye went to the desert waste. Alone in the desert, he cried, "Oh God, I know that you are good. Send me five thousand dollars. This will pay my debts and leave enough for the rest of my life." Tesfaye waited in the desert, but God sent no money.

Tesfaye went into the forest near his village. In the forest, he cried, "God, you are kind. Send me two thousand dollars. This will pay my debts and leave me some money to start as a merchant." He waited, but no money came.

Tesfaye grew desperate. He ran into the market place. There in the market, in front of everyone, he cried, "God, send me a thousand dollars. This will pay my debts. I will work hard to stay out of debt." Tesfaye waited but no money came.

The people were angry with Tesfaye and drove him from the market. They cried at him, "You have insulted God. He would not reward the lazy. You should expect nothing from Him."

Tesfaye went away to the forest to weep alone. He stood under a great tree and cried out in a loud voice, "God, there is nothing for me. My friends are against me. My business is gone. I have no money. Kill me!"

In the upper part of the tree, a poor woodsman was cutting dead branches for firewood. When Tesfaye cried out in a loud voice the woodsman was so frightened he dropped his ax.

The ax crashed down through the branches and narrowly missed Tesfaye's head. Tesfaye cried out, "God, when I ask for money I get nothing. When I ask You to kill me, You try to do it. Why do You hear me at the wrong time?"

THE ANT AND THE TOWER TO GOD

A very wise and just king ruled one of the kingdoms of baboons. This king was so wise and so just that all of the baboons in other kingdoms heard of him. The baboons in the other kingdoms said, "We wish this great one to be our king. He is the wisest and most just of all baboons. He should be the king of us all." All of the baboons of the other kingdoms dismissed their kings. They asked the wise and just baboon to rule over them all.

So the king ruled over all baboons. He ruled with wisdom and justice, and all of the baboons loved him greatly. Even the smaller and more foolish animals loved the baboon king. They asked that he be their king too. But the other baboons would not permit this. "Why do ants and worms and little things need a wise baboon as their king? They are not great animals. This is our king."

After many years the king grew old and sick and finally died. All of the baboons wept and cried at the loss of their great king. But they forbade other animals to weep for the king.

"He was *our* king," they told the others. "Only we have the right to cry for him."

The baboons gathered to have a great funeral feast. All the baboon chiefs gave speeches. They told of the great wisdom and justice of their king. After much crying and many speeches, one chief rose and said, "We must do something wonderful for our great king. His memory must be held high. What is the greatest honor we can pay him, now that he is dead?"

One wise old chief answered, "We can take his body directly up to God. That would be a great honor."

"How can we do that?" the others wondered. "God is in heaven. How can we get up there?"

"If we all work together very hard, we can do it," the old baboon said. "Anything is possible for creatures with hands. We can build a tower to God."

The baboons set to work to build their tower to God. But everything they used to build the tower crumbled. The wood rotted and split. The iron rusted. And the stones tumbled down. The old, wise baboon said, "We must put ourselves into this. Other things will not do. We must get all of the baboons of the world together. Then we can build a tower to God with our very bodies. One baboon can get on the back of another and so on until our baboon tower reaches to heaven."

The baboons from all the world were gathered. They climbed, one on top of another, and the tower began to stretch up toward heaven.

Now a small ant had been traveling from a distant country to mourn the death of the great king of baboons. The
ant traveled slowly. He had not heard that it was for-
bidden to mourn for the king of baboons. Most of the
words of the baboons went over the head of the tiny ant.

The ant arrived at the place where the baboon tower
was almost built. The ant tried to call up to a big baboon
who was about to climb up and form the top of the

tower. "Sir," the ant called. "Sir, one moment please."
But the big baboon ignored him. The baboon felt
very important. He was going to form the top of the
tower. He had not time for a silly little ant.

The ant walked over to the wise old baboon who was
supervising the building of the baboon tower. "Sir," the
ant cried. But the wise old baboon was looking only up.
"You up there near the cloud," he called. "Straighten
your shoulder or the whole thing will lean too much. All
right, lads, climb up there. We're almost up to heaven."

The ant called again, "Sir, I'm sorry . . ." but the wise
baboon ignored him.

Finally, the ant walked over to the base of the baboon
tower. He saw the feet of the great baboon who formed
the base of the tower. This baboon was a huge strong
fellow who held up all of the other baboons on his shoulder. The ant knew that his own little voice would not
carry up to this huge baboon. So the ant, to get the attention of the great baboon, stung him on the foot. The
baboon jumped, and the whole tower crumpled and fell
to the ground with a crash.

As baboons tumbled down all around him, the ant
cried as loudly as he could, "I am sorry to hear about the
death of your great king."

The Guragies tell this story to show that even the smallest and meanest of creatures have a right to show love
and respect for God. The little ant finally delivered his
message, and the proud baboons fell.

SEVEN

The Shankilla

We traveled to the country of the Shankilla. Shankilla country is in the steaming valley of the Didessa River. We traveled west from Addis Ababa, through Galla country to Gimbi. We went along the Gimbi-Mundi Road and cut off through the Ullaganti District to the Didessa valley. And we were in the country of the Shankilla.

The Shankilla are not as other people think they are. The Gallas say of the Shankilla people: "They are fierce and black. They will kill you." The Shankilla are black, but they are not fierce, and they did not try to kill us.

Americans and Europeans in Ethiopia say that the Shankilla are the wildest and most primitive of tribes. The Shankilla are primitive, but they are not wild. They are big, easy-going people who have been pushed about by other Africans for many years. The Shankilla wish to be left alone. They wish to tend their gardens down in the hot valley and feed themselves.

If the Shankilla need money to buy iron for spears, or powder and bullets for their guns, they sell cotton. Cotton grows well down in the hot Didessa valley. The Shankilla sell their cotton in the Galla markets and then hurry back to their valley. They have reason to hurry back. For years the Shankilla have been the prey of the slave raiders.

The fierce Taureg raiders coming down from North Africa have taken many Shankilla slaves. The Tauregs have taken the Shankilla from their homes, chained them together, and marched them north and west to die on the desert or live in slavery somewhere far from home. This would make any tribe fearful and suspicious.

The Shankilla wish to live in peace, but they do not trust other people. Because they do not trust other people, the Shankilla have not sent their children to missionary schools or government schools. The Shankilla live alone, with their own languages and customs and religions. But the Shankilla are not fierce people. A story of our own may show why we do not think the Shankilla are wild or dangerous.

WE KILL THE SNAKE GOD

THERE are no hospitals in the Shankilla country. There are no doctors there or nurses or even any medicine. Each year one medical missionary and his wife travel through the Shankilla country helping the people. Many people have the chills and fevers of malaria, and they die from this, shaken to pieces. Many Shankilla have the dread sleeping sickness. They sleep and drowse and finally

die. Many Shankilla have enormous jungle sores that cover
their legs.

We were in the Shankilla country when the missionary
and his wife were there. They came to our camp at night.
They wished to borrow one of our rifles. And why
do missionaries want to borrow rifles? They wanted to
kill a snake. Not a small snake, but a very big snake. They
wanted to kill a large python that lived near a village on
the river.

The missionaries had come to the village on the river
the day before to treat the sick and injured Shankilla
there. One boy that was brought to them had a badly
mangled leg. The villagers said that the boy had fallen.
But the missionaries knew that this was not true. The
boy's leg had been chewed by teeth.

The villagers then said that the boy's leg had been
mangled by a leopard. But the missionaries knew that
this too was a lie. A leopard strikes from behind and
above and pulls its game down. The leopard jumps from
above. The victim is clawed on the shoulders and neck
as the leopard leaps from the branch of the tree. The missionaries did not believe the villagers' story of the leopard. So the boy who helped the missionaries went through
the village to learn what had really happened. He learned
the truth. The boy's leg had been mangled by the teeth
of a great snake.

The boy had worked as the assistant of the village
witch doctor. The boy's job was to bring food each day
to the hole of the snake, on the river bank. The witch
doctor worshiped this snake. The snake was the witch

doctor's power. People from the village had to take turns
sending food to the snake. The witch doctor took his
share of the food and sent the rest to the snake. The boy
brought the food and left it at the mouth of the hole.

But one day the snake attacked the boy. It grasped his
leg in its mouth and chewed. The boy broke away from
the snake and got back to the village. The servant of
the missionaries learned that the father of the boy was
very angry. He was going to kill the witch doctor. The
missionaries talked to the father. They said, "Don't kill
the witch doctor. He is a poor ignorant man who believes
in the power of snakes. Kill the snake."

We walked to the village in the early morning, through
the damp forest. The father of the boy led us to the hole.
We set up our rifles and waited. At midday the snake
came out into the sun. We killed the snake.

The villagers heard the firing. They ran to the river
bank, and we showed them the dead snake. The witch
doctor cried and tore his clothes to pieces. But the people
did nothing. They said, "The snake bit the boy. These
people killed the snake. The other ones will make the boy
well. That is as it should be."

We know the Shankilla are not fierce or dangerous people. They made no move to harm us when we killed their
snake. We listened to their stories, and some of their
stories were what we would expect of such people. They
tell of the strong attacking the weak and of people not
acting the way they should. Remember that the Shankilla
are a tribe who have known much trouble and sorrow.

THE PEACE BETWEEN THE LEOPARD
AND THE ANTELOPE

A LEOPARD and an antelope lived in the same forest and drank at the same river. Often the leopard waited for the antelope and tried to kill him when he passed through the forest. But the antelope was large and had great sharp horns and heavy hoofs. The antelope always managed to fight off the leopard. Finally the antelope began to attack the leopard first, and both animals wounded each other badly.

One day the antelope and the leopard had a terrible fight. The antelope tore a big hole in the leopard's side. The leopard cut the antelope's shoulder to the bone with his claws. Both animals were badly hurt and stayed deep in the forest waiting for their wounds to heal.

When the leopard's side had healed he went to visit the antelope. The leopard spoke in a friendly way to the antelope. The leopard said, "It is not wise for us to fight this way. You are a strong and brave antelope. If we fight, neither of us can win. And perhaps both of us will become weakened and be eaten by the hyenas. We should live in peace in this forest."

"That is very well," the antelope said. "But I always wished peace. You attacked me first at the water hole."

"That is true," the leopard said. "It is my nature to attack first. I am sorry that I attacked you. Let us have peace. I promise not to attack you again. You promise not to attack me."

"I am not certain if that is a good agreement," the antelope said. "How do I know that you will keep your promise? One day when I am drinking at the river, you might kill me from behind."

"I swear that I will not do that," the leopard said. "But if you still do not trust me, we will make a peace agree-

ment. If one of us attacks the other, the sin will be visited on our children's children. If you attack me, then your children's children will suffer. If I attack you, my children's children will suffer."

"Agreed," the antelope said. "If one of us attacks the other, the sin will be paid for by our children's children."

For many days after the agreement, the leopard and the antelope lived in peace. They became friends. The antelope grew heavy and sleek from sleeping in the shade of the deep bush. The leopard grew fat and happy, and his hunting went well. The antelope went about without fear and ate the very best leaves from the bushes, wherever he wished. The leopard hunted other easier animals and did well.

One evening when the antelope was returning along a jungle trail from the water hole, the leopard happened to be waiting in a tree above the trail. It was nightfall and the leopard had waited in the tree all day to catch a fat monkey. But the monkey had escaped to the high branches. The leopard was hungry and he saw the antelope and thought, "How big and fat he is! He would be a meal for three days. Antelopes are supposed to be the food of leopards. This one has no right to be fierce and strong. He is not natural. He should be killed."

When the antelope passed under the tree, the leopard sprang at his back. But the leopard sprang so far that he went over the antelope's back and landed on his sharp horns. The antelope threw the leopard from his horns. Then the antelope stomped on the leopard with his sharp hoofs.

As the leopard lay dying on the ground he said, "You will be sorry for this. The sin of this will be on your children's children."

The antelope answered, "How do you know that your trouble now isn't because of the sins of your father's father?"

The antelope's reply seems a good one. Probably the dying leopard's trouble had come from the sins of his grandfather. Perhaps his grandfather had killed an antelope that wasn't as strong as the one in this story. The story doesn't tell us whether or not this is so. But it does point out that for the violators of peace agreements, no sympathy is necessary. The leopard got what he deserved. Not only was he killed, but the antelope even got in the last word.

THE UNGRATEFUL SNAKE

A MERCHANT once traveled from Yubdo to Nekemti in the time of the great rains. At Ganti, the water of the Didessa River was very high and the merchant had to build a shelter and wait for the water to go down. Every morning the merchant drove his largest mule into the river to measure the depth of the water. The merchant had decided to cross when the river water ran below the bottom of the mule's pack. For many days the merchant drove his mule into the water; but each day the river climbed high on the mule's back, and the merchant went back to his shelter to wait.

Now a fat lazy snake often came out on a rock by the
river bank to lie in the morning sun. From his rock, the
snake watched the merchant test the water of the river.
At first the snake scarcely looked at the merchant. But
finally the snake became interested. Why, he wondered,
does this man wish to cross this river? Is it not the same
on the other side?

The lazy snake had never bothered to swim across the
river to see the other bank. Still, when the man came every
day and tried to cross, the snake wondered what was on
the other side.

One day the river water did not come up to the pack
saddle. The merchant returned to his shelter and loaded
his mules for the crossing. The snake had watched all this.
The snake coiled lazily down from his high rock and
moved toward the man. When the snake approached the
mule train, the mules reared and began to snort and back
with fear. But the man was not afraid of snakes — particu-
larly lazy ones. "Ho, master snake," the merchant cried.
"You are sleek and fat. What do you want from me, Fat
One?"

Now the snake was not happy at being called "fat."
But he showed no sign of anger to the man. He answered
sweetly, "You seem to be ready to go across. Can I cross
with you?"

"Swim," the man advised him. "That's what snakes are
supposed to do."

"Aya! I can't do that. The river still runs too fast for
me. Let me cross on the back of one of your mules."

"All right," the merchant agreed. "Crawl up on the pack there."

But none of the mules would let the snake ride on their packs. When the man tried to place the snake on the mule's back, the mule pitched and reared and bucked.

"Won't anyone trust a poor snake?" the snake cried. "We are without friends. Even a silly mule will not trust us."

Now the merchant was a kind-hearted man. His heart was still full of thanks to God because the water had gone down in the river before his food was gone. The man said, "All right, master snake. Crawl up on my head. I will take you across the river."

The man and the mules and the snake crossed the Didessa River. The snake enjoyed the ride across the river. He had never enjoyed such a fine view from such a high perch. From the top of the man's head the snake could see more than he had ever seen from his rock on the river bank.

When they reached the opposite shore, the snake looked down and saw the river bank. It was much the same as the bank on the other side of the river. There were mud and stones and a few rushes by the edge of the water — nothing really different. "All right, master snake," the man said. "Crawl down, and I'll be on my way."

"I see no reason to get down," the snake said. "There's nothing on this bank different from the one I just left. You've tricked me. You got me all the way over here for nothing. I prefer to stay up here where I am."

The man and the snake argued long and loud, but the snake refused to get down. The snake enjoyed his high seat on the top of the man's head.

"All right," the man said. "The high court is now meeting in Nekemti. We will go there. The judge will order you down."

"Very well," the snake said. "We'll leave it up to the judge. I'm sure he'll see that I am right. You tricked me. I thought this side of the river would be different. Now I'm separated from my family and you are to blame."

The merchant from Yubdo and his mules arrived in Nekemti and went to the square where the court was in session. But the court, as always, was very busy and the merchant and the snake had to wait. Day after day they waited. The snake moved restlessly about on top of the man's head. The snake could hardly wait to tell his side of the story. But nobody in the court would listen to them. There were many unusual and interesting cases before the court, and the snake and the man were told to wait their turn.

One day a jackal was passing by and he noticed the snake on the man's head. The man and the snake told the jackal their stories.

"Well, you're silly to wait around the court of men," the jackal said. "Your case can end only one way here. You both will die of old age from waiting. Come into the forest and you can appear before the animal court."

"But they will decide against me," the man protested. "They will judge in favor of the snake, who is one of them."

The jackal was angry at this. "Hold on," he cried. "The snake is not one of us. The snake is a snake — that is all. Just a snake. You are one of us. The snake isn't."

At the animal court, all of the beasts of the forest were gathered before Judge Elephant. But the jackal pushed through the crowd. "I think we have an unusual case here," he cried. "Here is a snake who will not leave this man's head."

All the animals agreed that this was an unusual case. They agreed to hear the case right after Judge Elephant had his dinner.

Judge Elephant ate a large dinner and while they waited the snake fell asleep. The man tried to sleep, but it was difficult to sleep with the snake on his head. Instead, the man talked to the jackal, who never slept.

"I've got to get this bad snake down from my head," the man said. "It's worth anything to me. I can't go to my home with a snake on my head."

"I think I can get the snake down," the jackal said. "But it will cost you something."

"Anything," the man agreed. "Anything you ask."

"I will come for my reward tonight," the jackal said. "I will come to the edge of the village."

"Agreed," the man said.

Judge Elephant blew a blast on his trunk, and the court began for the afternoon. As the man and the snake came before Judge Elephant, the jackal stood on his tip-toes and whispered to the snake, "You look foolish. You cannot plead your case from up on that man's head. Get

down and act dignified. You will please Judge Elephant
better if you act right."

The snake crawled down from the man's head as the
man began to tell his story. Judge Elephant looked very
puzzled. "I see no snake," Judge Elephant rumbled.
"Where is the snake you are talking about?"

Judge Elephant stumbled forward to see the snake
on the man's head. And Judge Elephant put his huge foot
down on the snake's head and killed it. "There is no
snake on your head," the judge roared at the man. "I see
no snake. Get out of my court. Case dismissed."

"I will claim my reward tonight," the jackal told the man.

That night the merchant began to worry. The jackal could ask anything of me, the merchant worried. How do I know what he will want? He could want all of my goods and mules. The jackal is an animal, like the snake. You can't trust any of them.

That night the man brought a pack of dogs to the edge of the village. When the jackal came to get his reward, the man set the dogs on him. As the dogs chased him, the jackal cried out to the merchant, "You are as bad as the snake. You are ungrateful. I got the snake to get down from your head."

"Do not say such foolish things," the merchant cried. "Who ever heard of a snake on a man's head? What could be more foolish and silly?"

"A jackal that trusted a man," the jackal replied.

EIGHT

The Ancient Land of Tigre

In Axum, the holy city, almost three thousand years ago the kingdom of Ethiopia had its beginning. Then it was called the Axumite kingdom. Its people built palaces and monuments when their kingdom was powerful. Then, like other great civilizations, Axum's glory faded away. Today we have only ruins of its great past.

Who built the great stone monuments, so perfect in workmanship and taller than the famous obelisks of Egypt? No one knows. When were they put up? No one knows this, either, though it was probably before Ethiopia became a Christian country. How were these great stones dug and how were they set upright? The answers to these questions have not yet been discovered.

To the most important question of all — why were these monuments put up? — we do know at least part of the answer. The crescent or quarter moon shape at the top was the symbol of the Greek god Ares. Coins that have

been found in Axum make it clear that there was trade
between the early Greeks and this ancient African kingdom. The Axumites raised stone monuments to Ares.

But the god Ares did not last. In the fourth century,
one of the Axumite kings became a believer in Jesus, and
he spread Christianity to all of his people. Thus Ethiopia
became one of the first Christian countries in Africa.

It is because Ethiopian Christianity was born in Axum
that it is considered the holy city of Ethiopia. Almost to
the present day, all emperors of Ethiopia have come to
Axum to be crowned; the priests at the ancient church of
Mary of Zion in Axum are caretakers of a priceless collection of imperial crowns. And the church itself has on
its walls some of the most unusual religious art in the
world.

The early Christians of Ethiopia were not to be out-
done by their ancestors who had put up the great monuments to the god Ares. These Christians decided to build
something for their God that would last until the end of
time. They went to places in Tigre where there are great
stone cliffs. They chiseled out gigantic chunks of the
cliffs and then slowly and painfully hollowed out the in-
sides to make churches, at the same time making beautiful arches, pillars, and interior decorations.

In Tigre today there still exists one of the oldest and
strangest monasteries in the world. A monastery is a place
where men live all their lives together, praying and thinking about God. The monastery of Debra Damo in Tigre
was founded over fifteen hundred years ago. It is built on
a flat-topped mountain, surrounded on all sides by sheer

cliffs that cannot be climbed by any man or animal. To reach the monastery a person must be hauled up by a rope, and to leave it he must be lowered in the same way.

If a person can only reach this mountaintop by being pulled up with a rope, perhaps you are wondering how the very first man got there. It is a good question, but it is another one of the many mysteries of Tigre. The monks of Debra Damo will tell you that the monastery was founded by Abba Aragawi. They will tell you that as he stood at the base of the mountain longing to get to the top, a great snake came out of the ground. At the same moment St. Michael appeared by Abba Aragawi's side. At the saint's command the snake took the Abba in his coils and gently drew him to the top of the mountain. That is what the monks believe, and who is there to prove to them that it did not happen in this way?

Of course not all of the people of Tigre today are priests or monks or nuns. As in the other parts of Ethiopia, most of them are farmers and shepherds. The mountains of Tigre are among the highest and most rugged in Ethiopia, and the mountain farmers must plant their crops on slopes that sometimes seem to be almost straight up and down. You wonder how they can harvest their *sindi* or wheat without falling into the "valleys of dreadful depth," as one early traveler in Ethiopia called them.

As you might guess, many of the stories that the people of Tigre tell have to do with God or His wisdom. Others make some point about the right and the wrong way to behave. But even though the stories teach a lesson they are not all solemn and serious — as you will discover when you read this first Tigrian story about how God helped Mammo.

HOW GOD HELPED MAMMO

IN the village of Adi Ugra in Tigre there lived a man named Mammo Bulgala. Without doubt he was the laziest man in the whole of Ethiopia, and perhaps in the whole world. Although he was big and healthy, he did not work; in fact, he had never worked a day in his whole life. Yet he was the fattest man in the village because he was a clever talker. He could always manage to talk a neighbor out of some food or a stranger out of some money. With his gift for talking, Mammo could have been a great leader of his people if he had not been so lazy.

On top of a rather high mountain near Mammo's village stood another village named Masheela. Once each year the people of Masheela held a great feast in honor of Saint Tekle-Haimanot, the most beloved of all Ethiopia's saints. Although he was never invited, Mammo was always on hand on Saint Tekle-Haimanot's feast day. And though he never brought any food, he always ate more than the three biggest eaters in Masheela put together. The people of Masheela would have run him out of the village; but with his great gift of talking, Mammo always convinced them that it was their Christian duty to let a visitor share the feast foods.

The day for the feast had come again, and Mammo set out for the mountaintop village. He was especially hungry on this day. His mouth watered as he thought about the different kinds of *ziggany* (hot sauces) with sheep, chicken, and beef swimming in them. He thought about the great stacks of *injera* he would devour.

You would have thought that Mammo would be happy as he walked toward this delicious free dinner, but he wasn't. And that was just the trouble — he was walking. Since he never worked, he had no money to buy a donkey to ride; and certainly no one in his village would lend a valuable donkey to such a fat man.

After he had walked up the mountain trail for perhaps a mile, the sun became too hot for him to bear. Feeling very sorry for himself, he lay down in the shade of some bushes and slept for a while. When he awoke he felt better, and the sleep had given him a wonderful idea. Since he was such a great talker, he would speak to God about his troubles in climbing the mountain. He would explain to Him that he had to have help.

"God," he said in a loud voice (so that God would be sure to hear), "You know that I am a poor sick man who should not be walking in this hot sun. But I must get to Masheela to show my love for Saint Tekle-Haimanot. How am I to do this if You do not help me? Surely You can find some fast way to get me to the top of the mountain."

It was a fine speech and Mammo was very much pleased with himself. He closed his eyes and lay back in the shade. He waited for God to move him to the top of the mountain.

Now it so happened that while Mammo had been asleep, another man had come along driving a loaded

donkey. This man was named Ayele Ketaw (which just
happens to mean "The Power to Punish"). He was a big,
strong man and a great hunter. When he saw the lazy
Mammo sleeping, he himself decided to stop for a while
to give his donkey a rest. The beast lay down on the other
side of the bushes, out of Mammo's sight.

Ayele knew Mammo and was well aware of his great
laziness. He also knew that Mammo was on his way to
Masheela to eat the feast food, not to show his love for
Saint Tekle-Haimanot. When Ayele heard Mammo calling to God for an easy way up the mountain, he became
greatly enraged.

Ayele pulled up his *shamma* so that it covered his
face. He picked up the donkey's heavy load, stepped
through the bushes, and stood looking down at the lazy
fat man.

"Oh, Mammo," he said, "I have been sent to help you
up the mountain."

Mammo opened his eyes and sat up. "God has answered my plea very fast," he said, greatly pleased. "How
are you going to help me?"

"First," said Ayele Ketaw, "we must strap this bundle of
gazelle hides on your back."

"Very well," said Mammo, standing up, "but what good
will that do?"

"It is simple," said Ayele, quickly tightening the straps.
"The load on your back will balance your great stomach
in front."

Saying this, Ayele stepped back. He drew his thick-
bladed sword and let the *shamma* fall away from his

face. When Mammo recognized the mighty hunter and saw him draw his sword, he began to tremble.

"What are you going to do?" he cried.

"Help you up the mountain, like I said," Ayele answered. "You told God that you could not walk up the mountain. Very well, you shall not. Instead, you are going to run every step until you reach the top!"

With these words Ayele stepped forward. He gave Mammo a great smack on the bottom with the flat of his sword. "Now run," he said, "and if you stop, you shall feel the point of this sword."

Mammo ran. Oh, how he ran! The trail was steep here, but his feet fairly flew over it as he heard the singing sound of Ayele's sword cutting the air close behind him. Mammo was very quickly out of breath, however, and was about to stop and beg for mercy. But just at that moment his leg brushed against a thorn bush, and he thought it was the point of Ayele's sword. He burst forward even faster, and it was almost five minutes before the hunter could catch up with him.

The trail grew steeper, but Mammo heard Ayele's step behind him again. He kept running. The people along the trail stopped to stare at them in amazement. And it was indeed a strange sight — Mammo galloping desperately along, the hunter at his heels swinging his sword, the little donkey trotting happily behind them, amazed that a human being should be carrying his load. But most unbelievable of all was to see Mammo running. It was a sight that no one in the country had ever seen before.

At last, when Mammo thought that he would surely

drop if he lifted his foot for one more step, the village of
Masheela came into sight. Then it took only a slight
tap of the sword to send Mammo staggering over the last
rise and onto the very top of the mountain.

At the edge of the village Mammo collapsed under
a tree. He lay with his eyes closed, gasping for breath.
He was much too tired even to groan.

Ayele stood over him and put his sword back in its
scabbard. "Now, my fat friend," he said, "you have
reached the top of the mountain without walking, just
as you wished. This will teach you, I hope, that God hears

the prayers of men. Always be sure, therefore, that what
you ask for is what you really want."

Ayele went into the village and joined the feast. Mammo,
on the other hand, fell into an exhausted sleep and did
not awaken until the last scrap of feast food had been
eaten. The villagers were very happy. For the first time
in many years they had enough food for everyone at
their feast.

And it is said in the village of Adi Ugra that Mammo
was never quite the same after the day that God helped
him up the mountain. He did not talk so much after
this. And sometimes — not often, to be sure, but sometimes
— he even worked to pay for the food he ate.

The next story is a favorite type of Tigrian tale. It is
very short, but it teaches a very plain lesson in a clever way.

THE PRIZE

A FEWERK and Makonnen were poor farmers; but they
were very rich in one way — their good friendship that
brought them much joy. They went everywhere together
and had been nick-named "the two eggs" by their neighbors because both men were bald, having not a single
hair on their heads.

One bright sunny morning Afewerk and Makonnen
walked side by side down the trail to the village. It was
market day. Neither had anything to sell nor so much as
a penny in his pockets. Still they would enjoy talking
with the people at the market.

"If I had half a dollar," Afewerk said longingly, "I would buy a fine dinner of *ziggany* and a whole bottle of *tej*."

"With that much money," said Makonnen, "I would buy —"

He never finished what he was going to say. Suddenly, both men saw the light reflecting from some bright object lying in the trail ahead. Thinking of nothing but a shiny silver half-dollar, they rushed forward to lay claim to it. Afewerk reached it first, but with a desperate leap Makonnen caught him. He tried to shove Afewerk aside. Afewerk pushed roughly at Makonnen. In an instant they were on the ground. They rolled over and over, hitting each other, and tearing their poor clothes to shreds. They choked in the dust, and sweat glistened on their bald heads.

From a distance one of the local priests had seen the two friends start their fight, and he now rushed forward. He pulled them apart and picked up the object they were fighting for.

"You silly scoundrels," he said in a terrible voice, "to lose your valuable friendship over *this*."

The priest held out to them a piece of a cheap metal comb. He looked at the two men pityingly, and they hung their heads in shame.

"Which of you," the priest asked, "would like to comb your hair first?"

We said that the lesson of this story is plain. But just what is the lesson? Is it that greediness leads to un-

happiness? Or is it that nothing is as valuable as a good
friend? Or does it prove the old saying that all is not gold
that glitters? Perhaps it says all of these things, and that
is why the Tigrians like it.

Probably the stories best known to all Ethiopians and
most loved are religious stories. There are hundreds of
these stories, and they are told in pictures on the walls
and ceilings of churches all over the country. Whether
the pictures are ancient or modern, they are all painted
in bright colors and in a primitive "flat" style, without
depth. Many of the stories are famous ones from the
Bible — the life of Jesus, Adam and Eve, Salome and
John the Baptist, Noah's Ark. One of the most popular
scenes is that of St. George slaying the dragon; St. George
is considered to be the patron saint of Ethiopia.

Many of the pictures tell religious stories that are
unknown to the rest of the Christian world. For hundreds
of years after Ethiopia became a Christian country, it was
isolated from the rest of the world by its towering mountains and waterless deserts. In fact, it became a forgotten
country and was thought of in Europe as the mythical
Land of Prester John. In this complete isolation it is easy
to understand how Ethiopia developed its own stories of
saints and sinners and marvelous events. There is the
story of Tekle-Haimanot, the most beloved of Ethiopian
saints, who prayed for seven years without sleep, standing
on one leg to keep himself awake, and eating nothing but
seven grains of wheat during the whole time. There is the
story of the girl who fell in love with the devil and went

to live with him in hell; and there is the story of the great *abuna* (head priest) who burned the waters of Lake Haik in order to show the sinful lake people the power of the Lord. The story which follows is typical of Ethiopia's many religious legends.

SAINT GABRE MANFAS
AND HIS ANIMALS

Long ago in Ethiopia a very religious woman gave birth to a baby boy. The baby looked normal and healthy, but his parents were greatly worried because he would drink no milk, not even his mother's, nor would he eat any of the soft foods made of bread crumbs or cereal. The only thing that the baby would take was water. Yet he lived and grew as strong and healthy as any other little boy in the village.

A year passed, and then two and three, but never did Gabre Manfas, for such was the boy's name, take anything but water. By this time Gabre's parents realized that their child must be especially blessed by God. There was no other way to explain how he could live on nothing but water. Soon all of the people in the country round about knew that God had sent a saint to live in their midst, and religious men and women from all parts of the country made pilgrimages to the boy's home.

As the young saint grew up, he continued to take nothing but water, and he spent most of his time reading the holy books and praying. He did not play with the other children and he avoided grownups as much as possible, even his own parents. When he was not praying or reading, he preferred to roam in the forests and talk to the animals. He had no fear, even of the leopards or hyenas, and all wild animals followed him unafraid.

One day a farmer and his son were driving a cow and a

sheep to Gabre Manfas's birthplace. They wished to
arrive on the young saint's birthday and present the
animals to the village priests for a sacrifice. Near the town,
however, they met a lion and a leopard, and both father
and son ran away leaving the cow and sheep behind. The
lion and leopard took these two animals to Gabre Manfas,
who was in the forest near by, and asked what should be
done with them.

Gabre Manfas said, "Take the cow and sheep deep into
the forest and feed them well for a year. Then on my
next birthday take them to the village and give them to
the head priest for sacrifice. The good farmer brought
them for the glory of God, and for this purpose they
should be used."

The lion and leopard did as Gabre Manfas wished. They
took the cow and sheep to a part of the forest where the
grass was best and the water purest, and they watched
over them day and night for a year.

At the end of the year the lion and the leopard drove the
cow and the sheep into the village and took them to the
church. All of the villagers fled in terror when they saw the
fierce jungle cats. Even the young priests fled. But the head
priest was unafraid. When he saw the lion and leopard sitting patiently tending the sheep and cow, he knew that they
must have been sent by Saint Gabre Manfas himself. Then
the villagers and young priests came back, and they were
amazed at the size of the two animals that had been brought
for sacrifice. The cow was almost as big as an elephant, and
the sheep was almost as big as a cow.

The two animals were butchered and the villagers cel-

ebrated the birthday of their saint with a great feast. Every
year since that time, even to this very day, priests accept the
fattest cows and sheep from villagers all over Ethiopia as
a sacrifice on the birthday of Saint Gabre Manfas.

After this feast Gabre Manfas set out on a long journey.
He traveled all over the country and the animals he had
known in the forests near his village went with him. As
they walked through the land, other animals followed
him, and he talked to all of them and was kind to them.

At last they came to a burning, waterless desert, and
they all were tortured with thirst. They came upon a small
black bird lying on the hot sands, its wings spread out, its
beak open in agony. The bird begged Gabre Manfas to
give it just one drop of water.

The saint was overcome with pity for the bird. "I have not even one drop of water," he said. "The only thing I can offer you to quench your thirst is my eyes. You may pick them open and drink from them."

The bird did so and from that time on he flew with Gabre Manfas wherever the saint might go. In the church pictures that tell the story of Saint Gabre, you will always find the scene of the bird drinking from the saint's eyes.

Many years passed and Saint Gabre became a very old man. At last the Lord sent His angel to tell the saint to prepare for death. Gabre Manfas was very sad.

"I should like to live to take care of my animals," he said. "Who else shall care for them?"

The angel returned and told God of the saint's desire

and God let him live. After another hundred years He
sent His angel again to Saint Gabre and told him to prepare for death.

"But my animals," said Saint Gabre. "They are still
with me. I have never eaten any living thing, either plant
or animal, and therefore I have not sinned. For this
reason I should not have to die."

Once more God let Gabre Manfas remain on earth, but
after still another hundred years, He sent the angel to
the saint.

"Will you not come with me and sit on the right of
God's throne in heaven?" the angel asked.

Now Saint Gabre knew that God must want him very
badly in heaven, so he said good-by to his beloved animals
and left them for his place in heaven.

When church artists paint the story of Saint Gabre
Manfas, they do not show him sitting on the right of God's
throne. They always show him wandering on earth with
his animals.

NINE

Falasha: The Mystery People

W̲ₑ call the Falasha the mystery people because the mystery of where they came from has never been solved. Anthropologists and ethnologists and archeologists have all worked on the problem, but they have not found the final answer. No one is sure where the Falasha came from, when they came to their present home in Ethiopia, and what race of people they really are.

The Falasha are called the "black Jews" of Ethiopia. The Falasha are certain that they are Jews. They believe that they came from the eastern end of the Mediterranean Sea, near the present countries of Israel and Jordan. But the Falasha are much darker in color than the people of Israel. We lived among the Falasha for a short time, and we could see very little difference between the Falasha and other African tribes.

The Falasha say that they came to Ethiopia in the time of King Solomon. They say that they came with the

Queen of Sheba when she returned to Ethiopia after a trip to Israel. The legend of Sheba and Solomon is one of the most ancient and best-loved stories in Ethiopia. The story is also very important in deciding who shall become king in Ethiopia. The Ethiopians believe that the story of Solomon and Sheba is true, and here is the way they tell it.

KING SOLOMON
AND THE QUEEN OF SHEBA

SOLOMON, the wise and wealthy, ruled over Israel a thousand years before the birth of Christ. Solomon by great wisdom and hard work extended his rule over land that stretched from the ancient city of Babylon to the ancient land of Egypt. From his capital in Israel, Solomon sent ships through the Mediterranean and through the Red Sea. The merchants on these ships spread the fame of Solomon, wisest and richest of ancient kings. The merchants told of the wonders of Solomon's palace and of the magnificence and holiness of the Yahweh temple built by Solomon as a wonder of the ancient world.

When Solomon ruled over Israel, the Queen of Sheba ruled over the highlands of East Africa. She heard of the wisdom, riches, and power of the great Solomon. She wished to visit the mightiest king of her time. She made up a great caravan and loaded it with gold, precious jewels, spices, and rich cloth. Then with many slaves and soldiers she set out for Israel, the land of Solomon.

The journey to Israel took many months. When Sheba

came to the court of Solomon, he was stunned by her
beauty, wisdom, and goodness. He fell in love with her.
Solomon wished to take Sheba as one of his wives. Many
times he asked her to be his wife. He invited her to stay
in the royal palace. She could not refuse this command
for fear of offending the king.

One night Solomon came to the chambers where
Sheba slept and urged her to be his wife. But still she
refused. Solomon then said that he would agree to bother
her no more, if she would agree not to take anything from
his palace except what he, himself, gave her. To this she
agreed. She was very rich, and she saw no need to take any
of Solomon's treasures. She agreed to become the wife
of Solomon if she took anything without his permission.

The next night Solomon sent many trays of rich and
heavily spiced food to the chambers of Sheba. He came to
dine with her. During the dinner he urged her to try dish
after dish of the rich and peppery food. After dinner,
Solomon rose and went back to his own quarters. As he
left he said, "Touch not the most common object without
my permission." Sheba smiled.

In the middle of the night Sheba awoke with a great
thirst, but wily old Solomon had sent no water to her
chambers. She crept out of her bedroom and took a jar of
water from another room. She drank the water.

At that moment Solomon entered her bedroom. He
said that she had broken her promise and had taken something without his permission. "Even though you took the
most common object rather than the most precious, this

object was not given to you. Therefore, you have broken
your promise."

Since she had broken her promise, she had to agree to
become the wife of Solomon. Sheba stayed in the court of
Solomon and his love for her beauty, wisdom, and goodness grew. But her people wished her to return to Ethiopia. Since she was a queen, she felt that it was her duty
to return to her people.

Finally, Sheba convinced Solomon that she must return
to Ethiopia. He showered her with riches and great gifts
for the journey. In her caravan he put the finest young
men chosen from the tribes of Israel. The Falasha say
that they are the descendants of the young Israelites sent
by Solomon to guard his beloved Sheba.

Back in Ethiopia, a child — the son of Solomon — was born to Sheba. She named him Menelik and raised him in the religion of the Israelites. To this day, the ruling house of Ethiopia traces its descent back to Menelik, son of Sheba and Solomon. Emperor Haile Selassie himself has in his veins the blood of King Solomon and the Queen of Sheba, according to Ethiopian belief. No king has ever been able to rule for long in Ethiopia unless he could prove that Solomon and Sheba were his ancestors.

According to their legends, the Falasha taught the religion of Israel throughout ancient Ethiopia. But in the fourth century after Christ, Ethiopia was converted to Christianity by a very forceful man named Frumentius. After that the Jews — presumably the ancestors of the present-day Falasha — were given the choice of adopting the new religion or being killed. Some of them became Christians, but most of them fled to the north and hid in the towering mountains of the Semien Range.

Later the Falasha were driven out of their mountains by King Alama Seged and his Ethiopian armies. The Falasha fled to the northern shores of Tana, Ethiopia's largest lake. Although they were still among their old Amhara enemies, this time they were allowed to live in peace. They had no king. They lived in poor and scattered villages.

At the time of the Civil War in the United States a British missionary, Reverend Henry Stern, visited the Falasha and worked among them. Reverend Stern reported that the Falasha at that time practiced a religion similar to the ancient religion of the Jews. He described them as industrious, clean, and healthy people.

The Falasha still tell tales of Biblical times and Biblical lands. They tell of their father Abraham and of Isaac and Jacob. The Falasha are proud of their ancestors of legend. Even today they keep many of the old laws and customs of the Jews, though some of their religious customs are different.

Did the Falasha really come from Israel? From their language, their appearance, and some of their customs, it seems that they did not. From parts of their religion, and according to their own beliefs and traditions, it seems that they did. The origin of the Falasha is one of the many mysteries of Ethiopia still waiting to be solved.

Most of the stories we heard in Falasha country were based on the Old Testament of the Bible. But they were not all like this. Some of the stories we heard there were new to us, and there was one about a gift that we liked very much.

THE GIFT AND THE GIVER

ONCE a poor farmer found a beautiful apple growing on a tree in his fields. The apple was so large, so shiny, and so well shaped that the farmer cried with joy when he saw it. Never had he seen such a beautiful apple on any tree in his country.

The farmer picked the apple, and wrapped it in his cloak, and brought it to his home. He showed it to his

wife and children, and they were as amazed as he was to
see such a beautiful apple.

Other farmers who lived in that village heard of the
apple and came to the house to see it. They too agreed
that it was a wondrous apple. Farmers from distant villages came to see the fruit. They touched it tenderly and
exclaimed in loud voices that it was a wonderful apple,
shaped to perfection by the hand of God.

After all had admired the apple, the question came —
what to do with it? The farmer wished to give it to his
favorite daughter. He said to her, "Truly, this is the only
thing that matches you in beauty. On both the fruit and
your fair face, the work of God's hand is clear. Take it
and eat of it, my beauty."

But the daughter was too modest. She said she was not
worthy of such a thing. She urged her father to take the
fruit for himself. It was given to him as a sign of God's
love and blessings. "It is worthy of a king," the daughter
said.

"You are right," the farmer agreed. "Why didn't I
think of that myself. Such a fruit is worthy of a king. I
will take it to the king. It is the only gift that I, a poor
farmer, can give that will be worthy of my king."

The farmer's wife wrapped the apple in the finest cloth
she had, and the farmer set out for the royal city. The
farmer carried the fruit very carefully in the cloth, and he
walked along the road slowly. After many days, he reached
the city, but the poor farmer could not get in to see the
king. The guards at the palace laughed at him and kept
him out.

"The king has thousands of fruit trees," they said. "Surely your fruit can be no more beautiful than that of the king."

The farmer opened the cloth and asked the guards to look. The apple was still as beautiful as the day it had been picked. The farmer would not let any of the guards touch the fruit. Finally they went away to call the commander. The commander admired the apple greatly, although the farmer would not let him touch it. The commander of the guard decided that he would bring the farmer to the chambers of the king.

When the farmer came before the king he spoke in this way: "Your Majesty, great King, beloved of all of us. I found a most beautiful apple on one of the trees of my field. It was such a wondrously beautiful fruit that men came from miles around to see it. I decided that only our beloved king could deserve such a thing. So I have carried this fruit a great distance from my house. And I wish to give it to you."

The king was greatly moved by the simple love of the farmer. "What would you have from me in return?" the king asked. "Name it, and it is yours."

The farmer was surprised. "I want nothing, but to see the joy on your face when you see this that God has made."

The farmer opened his cloth and showed the fruit to the king. "It is surely a work of God's hand," the king agreed. "Such size. Such color. Such a shine. It shines like a bright jewel."

The king called the queen and all of the family, and

they too marveled at the beautiful apple. While the people of the palace were admiring the apple, the poor
farmer left the court and started for his home. The king
noticed this.

"Where is that farmer?" he asked. "He has shown me
more love with this gift then anyone in the kingdom.
Ride after him. Take my best horse and give it to him.
Tell him the horse is from a grateful king, who has
learned a new lesson in kindness."

The servants rode after the farmer and found him
plodding along the road. The farmer was very happy
with the gift which he had not expected. He rode away
toward his village.

Word travels fast in a palace. Soon all the people in the
royal city learned that the king had given his best horse
to a poor farmer — and in exchange for a mere piece of
fruit.

A rich merchant of the town heard the story of the
king's gift. The merchant began to scheme. He thought,
"That poor farmer gave the king a simple apple from a
tree. And the king gave him his best horse in exchange.
What would the king give me if I gave him a horse? He
might give me his daughter. Or perhaps some valuable
jewels!"

The merchant picked the finest horse from his stable
and led it up to the gates of the palace. "I have a gift for
the king," the merchant told the guards. The guards let
the rich merchant in at once.

The merchant went before the king. "I have heard that

you have given your own horse to a farmer," the merchant said. "For that reason, I have brought you a fine horse from my stable."

"Thank you very much," the king said.

The merchant moved restlessly, first standing on one foot and then another. The merchant stroked his beard and looked worried. "Did you want something of me?" the king asked. The merchant stared down at the floor and did not meet the king's eyes.

"Ah, I see," the king said. "You have given me a gift. Now you expect something in return. Very well. Wait right here."

The king left the room. The merchant could hardly hide his joy. "It will be the jewels," he thought. "He has gone to get the jewels. I'm sure it will be the jewels."

The king returned carrying something wrapped in a rich cloth. "Take this apple," the king said. "It is most precious to me because it was given by a man who expected nothing in return. But you may have it."

The rich merchant was stunned. When he opened up the cloth he saw the perfection of the apple, but he paid no attention to its beauty. The merchant walked angrily out of the palace. When he was outside, he threw away the fruit. He began to pull out his beard and wail in a loud voice.

The king ordered his guards to drive the merchant from the palace grounds. "Tell him," the king said, "that a gift is only as good as the heart of the giver. A man should give without expecting a gift in return. Any other gift is worthless."

The king looked at the beautiful horse the merchant had brought him. "The merchant's horse is worthless as a gift," the king said. "As something to ride on, however, it seems to be a very fine horse."

TEN

The Somalis:
Wizards of Lion Country

THE Somalis live in the hot, semiarid lands between the Ethiopian Highlands, the Red Sea, and the Gulf of Aden. The Somali people are divided into many different tribal groups — the Gere, the Ogaden, and many others. The Somalis of the dry plains of the Ogaden are noted for their fierceness. It is said that they are very fond of white Moslem skull caps, and that they will not hesitate to collect the skull along with the cap, if necessary!

The Somalis are handsome people. The women are slender and graceful, and the men are tall. Their minds are quick, and their tempers are quick. The Somalis are among the cleverest of the African people. But they are still superstitious. For example, they do not like to have people take their pictures. They think the picture will be taken across the sea to Arab lands and that they will become prisoners of an evil eye.

The main Somali town is Jigjigga, and it seems that the
wind always blows here. The wind carries fine dust, and
the Somalis wrap their cloaks over their faces. When people talk in the big open market at Jigjigga, they often
squat and speak from behind their cloaks. We visited the
market and talked to a camel driver who squatted
against the dried mud wall of a building. The wind drove
sand and dust everywhere, but we talked for a long time.
The Somalis have many stories that come from Arab
countries and from India. They are fond of stories that are
puzzles or riddles. Here is one story that the camel driver
told us.

THE THREE SUITORS

THREE men were in love with the same woman. All three
men were of equal rank and wealth. All three men asked
for the girl's hand.

You would think that such a thing would gladden the
heart of the girl's father. But this was not so. Instead of
being glad, the father's heart was full of grief. No matter
how he chose, he was sure to offend two of the country's
most powerful men. Of course, the girl herself had no
choice, nor did she say which of the three she loved. So
the father had to worry alone.

Each day the fathers of the three men urged the father
of the girl to make a choice of sons. But each day the
father of the girl put them off. He consulted the great
holy men of the country, and he looked in the Koran, but

he found no answer to his trouble. If he chose one of the boys, the other two boys' fathers were sure to be angry and injure him.

Finally the father decided that he would have a test of skill to determine the young man who would win his daughter's hand. Three of the oldest and wisest men of the village were chosen to judge the contest. Each young man was to do whatever he wished, to demonstrate his skill.

The first young man was the strongest of the three. This young man hoisted two heavy men on his shoulders and swam across the river and back. The village cheered this great feat of strength.

The second young man was very skillful with spear and rifle. This young man shot *chat* sticks out of the teeth of his friends. The man was so skillful that he shot a flying bird from the sky, and pierced a silver coin as it spun through the air. The villagers muttered and marveled at this great skill.

The third young man was beautiful above all men. It was not only his face and form that had beauty. This young man could play on the harp and sing, so that birds would pause in flight and wild beasts would stop their fearful cries to listen. This man played his harp and sang. All of the village maidens sighed and tore at their veils. All of the village young men grew angry.

After the third young man had performed, the wise old judges went to a coffee shop to make their decision. And what was their decision? Did it help the father of the girl? These wise and learned judges announced this decision. The first young man had performed the greatest feats of strength. The second young man performed the greatest feats of skill with a rifle. And the third young man was certainly the best musician of the three. This was a wise decision for the judges, but it helped the father of the girl not at all.

Days and months passed and the three young men grew so anxious that they pitched their tents on the bank of the river near the girl's house. Daily their fathers pressed the girl's father for an answer, so that their sons might return home and tend to their business and flocks again. But the girl's father could give no answer.

One day the girl was at the river washing clothes, and the young men were on the bank watching the girl. The girl slipped on the mud bank and rolled into the river. Instantly a crocodile swam toward her.

The harpist seized his harp and played beautiful music. The music charmed the crocodile, and he stopped and rolled in the water with joy. Meanwhile the hunter seized his rifle and shot the crocodile. And the strong young man jumped into the water and saved the girl before she was carried downstream.

They carried the girl to the house, and with the help of a wise doctor she regained the flush of life and began to breathe. As soon as she was awake, all three suitors began to argue.

"I should have her," the harpist claimed. "For I was first to act. If I had not charmed the beast, your efforts would have been wasted."

"False," the hunter cried. "Your music delayed the crocodile for only an instant. In that instant, I shot him. I should have her."

"Wrong, wrong, all of you," the strong man cried. "Even if she were saved from the crocodile, the river would have taken her. I took her from the river. She is mine. I am the only one who risked life and safety for her."

The camel driver stopped talking and smiled at us. "Did you like that story?" he asked.

"How did it end?" we asked.

"I don't know," the man said. "In life there are no perfect endings; problems just go on and on. Perhaps that is what this story tells us."

"But people don't like stories that have no endings," we said. "There must be an ending."

"All right," the camel driver agreed. "Here is your ending. The case went before the three wise judges again. The first judge said that the girl should go to the harpist. The second judge said that the girl should go to the hunter. The third judge said that the girl should go to the swimmer. There is your ending."

"But it isn't an ending," we said. "Nothing has been decided."

"Nothing is ever decided in this life," the camel driver said. "But here is another ending for you. The father, in desperation, finally decided to leave the choice up to the girl. From that time on, women have been allowed to choose their husbands. That will make the story interesting — but false."

"And how did she choose?" we asked.

The camel driver laughed. "She could not make up her mind," he said. "I like that ending. It has some truth in it."

"But it is not an ending," we said. "We are right back where we started."

The camel driver rose. "Good," he said. "Then I must

go. If you want an ending for that story, you must find it
for yourself."

He drew his cloak across his face and walked away. The
wind swept through the market place and piled dust
against us. The camel driver moved into the crowd and
was gone.

"We'll get the end of that story," we said. "Somewhere
in this country we'll find it."

We found many stories in our travels, but we did not
find the ending to the one about the three suitors. And so
we must tell you what the camel driver told us: If you
want an ending for the story, you must find it for yourself.

THE MAN WITH A LION HEAD
IN A CAN

We began this book with a story about a lion's whiskers.
It was a story we heard from the old hyena wizard in the
Somali country. To end the book we will return to the
Somali country, and again there is a story about a lion.
This time though it isn't just the lion's whiskers; it's the
whole head!

We had driven into Harar from beyond Jigjigga in
Somali country, and we had stopped along the road to
shoot some guinea fowl for our dinner. We brought the
guinea fowl to the hotel in Harar and asked the cook to
prepare them for our dinner. Now the guinea fowl of
Ethiopia is one of the most wonderful game birds in the
world. It is almost all white meat, and the meat is tender

and juicy. A full-grown guinea is bigger than a large chicken but not quite so big as a turkey.

We were waiting hungrily for the guinea to be brought to us, when another American came into the dining room. He came over to our table and asked us if we were Americans. We said that we were, and he told us a strange story — the story of a lion's head in a tin can.

This man — call him Mr. Prince — had shot a lion just the day before. The man had been ten days down in the Fawfon Valley. He and his native guides and one companion had built a *boma,* which is a hunting fort made of thorn bushes. Each night they took a young calf and staked it down in front of the *boma.* Each night they lay behind the *boma* and waited for a lion to come in after the calf. The men lay many nights behind the thorn fort, but no lion came. For lion hunters, patience is even more necessary than courage.

Now Prince was a busy man. He had allowed himself only fourteen days to kill his lion. After that he had to return to his business in America. When seven days had passed, Prince grew impatient. He blamed the man with him for his bad luck. He blamed the Somali guides who had been hired to help him kill the lion. Prince blamed everyone but himself. (We discovered these things much later when we talked to the Somali boys who had been on the hunting party.) The Somalis said that Prince was noisy in the night. He could not lie behind the thorn fort quietly. He had to be up prowling around. He coughed nervously and called out every hour to see that the men

were not sleeping. The Somali boys told us that any lion
that Prince would shoot would have to be a deaf lion. He
frightened away any lion that could hear. And as the days
and nights passed, Prince grew even noisier. He insulted
his companion. He insulted his Somali guides — and
Somali men do not like insults. Like the Danakil, they are
proud people. They dislike men who talk loud, men who
use their voices rather than their wits and strength.

Finally, Prince became so nervous that he fell sick. He
did not even go out behind the fort to wait for his lion. He
had only two more days and the trip would be over. He
lay in his tent and cursed the heat and the mosquitoes and
the Somalis and the luck. And that was the night the lion
came. The lion came in for the calf. The guides heard it
and crept to Prince's tent to wake him. Prince brought his
gun to the edge of the thorn fort. The Somali men lit one
torch; and in the reflected light, the lion's eyes shone.

But Prince had waited too long. He was nervous. He
committed an unpardonable sin in hunting. He gut-shot
the lion. Instead of aiming for the head or fore-shoulder,
Prince shot the lion in the stomach. The lion was badly
wounded and confused and went back into the bush. The
Somalis went after the lion, but Prince lagged back. The
Somalis did not like this either. Finally, they found the
lion and killed it.

And then the Somalis played a joke on Prince. They
told him to cut off the whole head. They did not tell him
to skin out the head. They told him to take the whole
head. In the morning, Prince drove back to Harar with
his lion's head. He wished to send the head up to Addis

Ababa to have it mounted by a taxidermist. But Prince did not know that his lion head would not last very long because it wasn't skinned out. He drove happily into Harar and out to the airport and delivered the head to the pilot of an Ethiopian Airlines plane. The head was wrapped in a large burlap bag. The pilot refused to take the head on his plane. The plane was carrying passengers as well as freight, and the pilot didn't want the head aboard.

Again Prince made a mistake. He threatened the pilot. A pilot is like the captain of a ship. On his plane he is the boss. Prince's threats did not budge the pilot. So Prince had to bring his head back to Harar. In Harar he found a tinsmith who sealed the head up in a large can. The next morning Prince brought the can out to the airport. But the pilot of that plane — a freight plane — had been warned by the other pilot. The pilot of the freight plane refused to take the head on board unless Prince could show his hunting permit. Prince had no hunting permit. He had left it behind in Addis Ababa.

We met Prince after the second pilot had refused to take out the head. Prince still had the head in the tin can, and the tin can was in his hotel room. We went up to his room to look at the can. Prince asked us if we would take the lion head back to Addis Ababa in our Land Rover. We did not know Prince and we felt sorry for his trouble. We agreed to take the head with us the following morning. But that night Prince had more trouble.

That night we visited Mohammed, the wonderful wizard of the *Budaber*. We watched Mohammed call in his

hyenas. When we came back to the hotel, Prince was there
and he was in even more trouble. The manager of the
hotel had ordered Prince to take the lion's head out of
there. Prince had no vehicle. He had already insulted his
companion who owned the hunting car. Prince asked us if
we would put the head in our Land Rover. We agreed to
this, but we warned Prince that the back of the Land
Rover was canvas and that thieves could cut through it.
We always unloaded our Land Rover at night. Prince was
too desperate to argue. We helped him load his precious
tin into the Land Rover. And from somewhere back in
the shadows a thief watched us. The thief saw Prince fuss-
ing and worrying over the tin, and the thief decided that
the contents must be valuable.

In the morning, our Land Rover was empty, and the
canvas was cut, and Prince's precious can was gone. When
Prince notified the police they laughed at him. Why, they
wondered, should anyone be excited about a canned lion's
head. They pointed out to Prince that by this time the
head would be worthless. But they promised to search the
old *Megalla* market in Harar.

In the late afternoon the police found the tin and what
was left of the lion's head. The can had been opened and
the head was ruined. It had been ruined even before that.
Prince carried the remains up to the yard of the hotel.
"We'll load it on your vehicle," he said. "We might be
able to save something of it in Addis."

But we had to refuse. We couldn't travel two days with
a smelly lion's head in our Land Rover. We loaded our

Land Rover and left Prince in the yard, still brooding about his lion's head.

Later we talked to the Somalis, and they laughed long and loud about Mr. Prince, the noisy lion hunter. They said, "There is a story that they tell out on the desert. The Danakil tell it and we tell it. The Danakil say that it is their story, but it probably comes from somewhere else — it is the story of the turtle who could not keep his mouth closed."

THE TALKATIVE TURTLE

THE turtle moves slowly on the ground. Birds fly and fish swim and antelope run. But the turtle creeps slowly.

A turtle had watched the birds fly and the fish swim and the antelope run. The turtle wished to move swiftly as the others did. Most of all the turtle wished to move through the sky as the birds did. The turtle wished to go swiftly and to fly high.

One day the turtle said to the eagles, "Take me into the sky with you. I wish to move swiftly and to fly high."

"It can be done," the eagles agreed. "You have strong jaws. If you grasp a stick very hard and hold on very tightly, we can fly with you in the sky. But you must never let go. Don't open your mouth."

The turtle agreed to this. The eagles took both ends of a stick, the turtle grasped the middle of the stick in his mouth, and the birds soared into the sky. The turtle hung on tightly to the stick. He enjoyed flying high and swiftly through the sky.

The eagles flew over a village, and swooped low to look at some school children playing in a field. They looked above and saw the flying turtle. "Look at that silly turtle!" the children cried. "Why is he not walking on the ground as turtles are supposed to?"

The eagles soared up again, but the turtle had heard the children. He shouted angrily at them. "I'm not a silly turtle. I can fly —"

When the turtle opened his mouth, he lost his hold on the stick and began to tumble toward the ground, shouting, "I can fly-y-y-y . . ." He kept saying it all the way until he hit the ground and was killed.

When the Somali had finished his story, we said, "The story makes it very clear that sometimes a person should keep his mouth shut. But we agree that the Danakil did not make up the story. It came first from India."

"The story tells a truth about life," the Somali said. "And the truth travels far."